Math **Diagnosis** and **Intervention** System

Booklet E

Problem Solving
in Grades K–3

Scott Foresman · Addison Wesley

Overview of Math Diagnosis and Intervention System

The system can be used in a variety of situations:

- **During School** Use the system for intervention on prerequisite skills at the beginning of the year, the beginning of a topic, or the beginning of a lesson. Use for intervention during the Topic when more is needed beyond the resources already provide for the lesson.
- **After-school, Saturday school, summer-school (intersession) programs** Use the system for intervention offered in special programs.

The system provides resources for:

- **Assessment** Diagnostic Tests are provided. Each Diagnostic Test assesses the content for a grade. Use a test at the start of the year for entry-level assessment or anytime during the year as a summative evaluation.
- **Diagnosis** An item analysis identifies areas where intervention is needed.
- **Intervention** Booklets A–E in Part 1 and Booklets F–J in Part 2 identify specific concepts and assign a number to each concept, for example, A12 or E10. For each concept, there is a two-page Intervention Lesson that provides an instructional activity followed by practice. References for the Intervention Lessons are provided in teacher materials for *en**Vision**MATH.*
- **Monitoring** The Teacher's Guide provides both Individual Record Forms and Class Record Forms to monitor student progress.

Editorial Offices: Glenview, Illinois • Parsippany, New Jersey • New York, New York

Sales Offices: Boston, Massachusetts • Duluth, Georgia • Glenview, Illinois
Coppell, Texas • Sacramento, California • Mesa, Arizona

ISBN-13: 978-0-328-31120-0
ISBN-10: 0-328-31120-0

20 21 22 V069 14 13

Table of Contents

Booklet E: Problem Solving in Grades K-3

Extra Information

Math Diagnosis and Intervention System
Intervention Lesson E1

Math Diagnosis and Intervention System
Intervention Lesson E1

Name ______________________

Extra Information

1. Omar has 5 red toy cars.
   ~~He has 4 books.~~
   He has 3 blue toy cars.
   How many cars does Omar have?

   5 + 3 = 8 cars

2. 16 ducks are swimming on the pond.
   ~~6 frogs are in the pond.~~
   9 ducks fly away.
   How many ducks are left on the pond?

   16 − 9 = 7

3. 6 turtles are sitting in the sun.
   5 turtles are swimming in the pond.
   ~~There are 3 lily pads in the pond.~~
   How many turtles are there in all?

   6 + 5 = 11 turtles

1. Read the problem to the children. Help them understand by asking: ***What do you know?*** Omar has 5 red toy cars, 4 books, and 3 blue toy cars. ***What do you need to find?*** Find how many cars Omar has.
2. Ask: ***Do you need all the information given in the problem to solve?*** no ***What information is extra, not needed?*** Omar has 4 books is extra information. Have children cross out the sentence about 4 books.
3. Help children plan and solve by asking: ***How can you solve the problem?*** Add 5 and 3; Have children write a number sentence and solve.
4. Help children look back and check by asking: ***Did you answer the right question?*** Yes; 8 is the number of cars Omar has.
5. Do the other problems similarly.

Intervention Lesson E1 **35**

Math Diagnosis and Intervention System
Intervention Lesson E1

Name ______________________

Extra Information (continued)

Cross out the extra information.
Solve the problem.

4. ~~The library is 3 blocks from June's house.~~
   June got 9 books on Monday.
   She took back 4 books on Saturday.

   How many books did she have left?

   9 − 4 = 5 books

5. Buddy has 11 markers on his desk.
   His friend gives him 3 more markers.
   ~~He has 6 pencils inside his desk.~~

   How many markers does he have in all?

   11 + 3 = 14 markers

6. Sandi found 12 shells at the beach.
   ~~Ira found 2 pails in the sand.~~
   Ari found 8 shells.

   How many more shells did Sandi find than Ari?

   12 − 8 = 4 shells

7. 15 books are on a shelf.
   2 books are on a table.
   ~~5 pictures are on the wall.~~

   How many books are there in all?

   15 + 2 = 17 books

36 Intervention Lesson E1

Teacher Notes

Ongoing Assessment

Ask: ***What is extra information in a problem?*** Extra information is information that is given but is not needed to solve the problem.

Error Intervention

If children have trouble writing number sentences,

then use B7: Joining Stories, B17: Separating Stories, B18: Comparing Stories, B25: Stories about Joining, B32: Stories about Separating, and B33: Stories about Comparing.

If You Have More Time

Have children write word problems with extra information. If necessary, encourage children to draw pictures to "write" their story problems. Then have them trade papers with a partner and solve the problem their partner created.

Two-Question Problems

Math Diagnosis and Intervention System
Intervention Lesson E2

Name ______________________

Two-Question Problems

1. Luisa has 6 colored beads. She gets 3 more. How many beads does she have in all?

   6 + 3 = 9 beads

   Luisa gives 2 beads to Maria. How many beads does Luisa have left?

   9 − 2 = 7 beads left

2. Kevin has 4 books. He gets 4 more books. How many books does he have in all?

   4 (+) 4 = 8 books

   Kevin gives away 3 of his books. How many books does he have now?

   8 (−) 3 = 5 books

1. Read the first part of the problem. Help children understand by asking: ***What do you know?*** Luisa has 6 colored beads and she gets 3 more. ***What do you need to find?*** Find how many beads Luisa has in all.
2. Help children plan and solve by asking: ***How can you solve the problem?*** Add 6 and 3; Have children write a number sentence and solve.
3. Read the second part of the problem. Ask: ***What do you know?*** Luisa has 9 beads and she gives 2 beads to Maria. ***How did you know Luisa has 9 beads?*** by solving the first part of the problem ***What do you need to find?*** Find how many beads Luisa has left.
4. Ask: ***How can you solve the problem?*** Find 9 minus 2; Have children write a number sentence and solve.
5. Help children look back by asking: ***How many questions did the problem have?*** 2
6. Do the other problem similarly.

Math Diagnosis and Intervention System
Intervention Lesson E2

Name ______________________

Two-Question Problems (continued)

Solve each problem.

3. There are 10 flowers in a vase. 6 are roses. The rest are lilies. How many are lilies?

   10 (−) 6 = 4 lilies

   Sally took out 2 lilies. How many lilies are left now?

   4 (−) 2 = 2 lilies

4. Alberto has 7 pencils in his box. He gets 4 more. How many does he have in all?

   7 (+) 4 = 11 pencils

   He gives 5 pencils to Wen. How many does Alberto have left?

   11 (−) 5 = 6 pencils

5. Eva has 12 markers. She gives 5 to some friends. How many does she have left?

   12 (−) 5 = 7 markers

   Eva's teacher gives her 3 more markers. How many markers does Eva have now?

   7 (+) 3 = 10 markers

Teacher Notes

Ongoing Assessment

Observe children to be sure they use the answer to the first question in order to answer the second question in each problem.

Error Intervention

If children have trouble writing number sentences,

then use B7: Joining Stories, B17: Separating Stories, and B18: Comparing Stories.

If You Have More Time

Have children use counters to act out each problem.

Multiple-Step Problems

Math Diagnosis and Intervention System
Intervention Lesson E3

Name ______________________

Multiple-Step Problems

1. Soccer practice is 45 minutes long. The team spends 10 minutes warming up and 15 minutes on drills. How much time is left for games?

   How many minutes does the team spend warming up and doing drills?

Step 1	Step 2
10	45
+ 15	− 25
25	20

   20 minutes

2. Niki had 12 stuffed animals and 6 dolls. She gave away 7 of the toys. How many toys did she have left?

   How many toys did Niki have in all?

Step 1	Step 2
12	18
+ 6	− 7
18	11

   11 toys

1. Read the problem to the children. Help them understand by asking: ***What do you know?*** Soccer practice is 45 minutes long, which includes 10 minutes to warm up and 15 minutes on drills. ***What do you need to find?*** Find how much time is left for games.
2. Help children plan and solve by asking: ***How can you find how much time is left for games?*** Find 45 minus the time spent warming up and doing drills. ***The problem has a hidden question. What do you need to find before you can subtract to find the time left for games?*** How many minutes does the team spend warming up and doing drills? Have students write the hidden question.
3. Ask: ***How can you find how many minutes the team spends warming up and doing drills?*** Add 10 and 15; Have children find the sum under step 1. ***Now, what do you need to subtract?*** 45 − 25; Have children find the difference under step 2. Ask: ***How many minutes are left for games?*** Have children write 20.
4. Help children look back and check by asking: ***Since practice is 45 minutes, should the time for games be more than 45 minutes or less than 45 minutes?*** less than 45 minutes ***Is 20 minutes less than 45 minutes?*** yes ***How did you solve the problem?*** Find and answer the hidden question.
5. Do the other problem similarly.

Intervention Lesson E3 **39**

Math Diagnosis and Intervention System
Intervention Lesson E3

Name ______________________

Multiple-Step Problems (continued)

Write the hidden question. Then solve.

3. Paco had 28 balloons for his birthday party. He gave away 21 at the party. After the party, 2 more burst. How many balloons did Paco have left then?

   Hidden Question:
   How many balloons did Paco have at the end of the party?

Step 1	Step 2
28	7
− 21	− 2
7	5

   5 balloons

4. Becky practiced piano 34 minutes Saturday morning and 16 minutes Saturday afternoon. If she also practiced 22 minutes on Friday, how many minutes did she practice in all?

   Hidden Question:
   How many minutes did Becky practice on Saturday?

Step 1	Step 2
34	50
+ 16	+ 22
50	72

   72 minutes

40 Intervention Lesson E3

Teacher Notes

Ongoing Assessment

Ask: ***How do you know there is a hidden question in a problem?*** Sample answer: There is a hidden question when you need to know something to solve and you can find it from information given.

Error Intervention

If children do not add and subtract correctly,

then use C4: Adding Two-Digit Numbers, C10: Two-Digit Addition, C17: Subtracting Two-Digit Numbers, and C22: Two-Digit Subtraction.

If You Have More Time

Have children work in pairs. Have one child say a multiple-step problem and the other one solve. Then have them change roles and repeat.

Use Data from a Table or Chart

Math Diagnosis and Intervention System
Intervention Lesson E4

Name ______________________

Use Data from a Table or Chart

1. 10:00
2. Book Balance
3. Cartwheels
4. 70 pounds
5. Tip
6. Fido

Silly Sports Day	
Time	**Activity**
9:30	Egg on a Spoon
10:00	Ball Bounce
10:30	Hopping Race
11:00	Book Balance
11:30	Lunch
12:30	Cartwheels
1:00	Tiptoe Race

Weights of 5 Dogs	
Buddy	X 70 pounds
Fido	43 pounds
Socks	X 35 pounds
Tip	X 60 pounds
Vinny	X 15 pounds

1. Introduce the schedule. Ask: ***What time does the Ball Bounce begin?*** Have children find Ball Bounce in the schedule table. Ask: ***What time is in the same row as Ball Bounce?*** 10:00 ***This means the Ball Bounce starts at 10:00.*** Have children write the time as the answer to item 1.
2. Ask: ***What begins at 11:00?*** Have children find 11:00 in the table. Ask: ***What activity is in the same row as 11:00?*** Have children write Book Balance as the answer to item 2.
3. Ask: ***What begins at the time shown on the clock? To solve, first you need to find the time on the clock. What time is shown on the clock?*** Have children find 12:30 in the table. Ask: ***What activity is in the same row as 12:30?*** Have children write Cartwheels as the answer to item 3.
4. Introduce the second table. Ask: ***How much does Buddy weigh?*** Have children write 70 as the answer to item 4.
5. Ask: ***Which dog weighs 60 pounds?*** Have children write Tip as the answer to item 5.
6. Ask: ***Which dog weighs more than 40 pounds but less than 50 pounds?*** Have children put an x next to each weight that is not more than 40 pounds. Then have them put an x next to each weight that is not less than 50 pounds. Ask what is left. Have children write Fido as the answer to item 6.

Intervention Lesson E4 **41**

Math Diagnosis and Intervention System
Intervention Lesson E4

Name ______________________

Use Data from a Table or Chart (continued)

Use the table to answer the questions.

Field Day	
Time	**Event**
1:00 – 1:30	Parade
1:30 – 2:00	Relay Race
2:00 – 2:30	Cross-Country Race
2:30 – 3:00	100-Yard Dash

7. What time does the Relay Race begin? 1:30

8. What begins at 2:30? 100-Yard Dash

9. What begins at the time shown on the clock?
Cross-Country Race

10. Pick three events and make a schedule for yourself.

Time	Event
10:00-10:30	
10:30-11:15	
11:15-11:45	

Check that students pick one event from each time period.

42 Intervention Lesson E4

Teacher Notes

Ongoing Assessment

Ask: ***How is information organized in a table?*** Sample answer: Things in the same row go together.

Error Intervention

If children have trouble reading the time on the clocks,

then use D5: Time to the Half Hour.

If You Have More Time

Have children work in pairs. Have each child make a table or chart and ask their partner questions about it.

Missing or Extra Information

Name ______________________

Missing or Extra Information

Sally's painting is 14 inches long and 12 inches wide. Julie's painting is 16 inches long. How much longer is Julie's painting then Sally's painting?

Solve by answering 1 to 7.

Answer 1 to 4 to **understand** the problem.

1. What do you know from reading the problem?
   Sally's painting is 14 inches long.
   Sally's painting is 12 inches wide.
   Julie's painting is 16 inches long.
2. What do you need to find?
   How much longer is Julie's painting than Sally's painting?
3. Do you have all the information you need to solve the problem? yes
4. What information is not needed to solve the problem?
   The width of Sally's painting is not needed.

Answer 5 and 6 to **plan and solve** the problem.

5. How can you solve the problem? Find 16 minus 14.
6. Solve. How much longer is Julie's painting than Sally's painting? 2 inches

Answer 7 to **look back** at how you solved the problem.

7. Is your answer reasonable? yes

Intervention Lesson E5 43

Name ______________________

Missing or Extra Information (continued)

How much wider is Sally's painting than Julie's?

Find out by answering 8 and 9.

8. Do you have all the information you need to solve the problem? no
9. What do you need to know in order to solve the problem?
   The width of Julie's painting is needed.

   So, there is not enough information to solve the problem.

Write the extra or missing information. Solve the problem if enough information is given.

10. Jason bought a red sweater and a black sweater. His change was $5. How much did Jason pay for both sweaters?
    Missing information: You need the price of the sweaters.

Write the extra or missing information. Solve the problem if enough information is given.

Use the graph for Exercises 11 and 12.

Favorite Pet

Number of Votes: 0, 2, 4, 6, 8, 10
Pet: Dog, Cat, Hamster

11. Turtles received 4 fewer votes than cats and 2 more votes than rabbits. How many votes did turtles receive?
    2 more votes than rabbits is extra information; 5 votes
12. How many more students voted for dogs than horses?
    Missing information: Horses are not pictured in the graph.
13. **Reasoning** Rose's painting is 12 inches long. Will it fit in a frame that has length of 12 inches and a width of 8 inches? Explain.
    There is not enough information. The width of Kim's painting is missing.

44 Intervention Lesson E5

Teacher Notes

Ongoing Assessment

Ask: ***What is the extra and missing information in the following problem? Mindy bought 4 tickets to the play and Kate bought 3 tickets. How much did Mindy's tickets cost?*** The fact that Kate bought 3 tickets is extra information. The cost of each ticket is missing information that is needed to solve the problem.

Error Intervention

If students have trouble deciding whether to add or subtract,

then use J8 or E25: Draw a Picture and Write a Number Sentence.

If You Have More Time

Have students write their own problem with extra information and draw a picture to illustrate it. Have them explain how to solve the problem on the back of the page, including naming the extra information. Collect all the problems and bind them in a book titled "Our Problem Solving Book." When you have a few extra minutes, use the problems as a filler.

Two-Question Problems

Math Diagnosis and Intervention System
Intervention Lesson **E6**

Name ______________________

Math Diagnosis and Intervention System
Intervention Lesson E6

Two-Question Problems

Max earns $9 for every hour he rakes leaves. It took him 2 hours to rake the leaves in his yard. How much money did he earn raking leaves? If he already had $26, how much does he have now?

Solve by answering 1 to 7.

Answer 1 and 2 to **understand** the problem.

1. What do you know from reading the problem?

Max earns __$9__ for every hour he rakes leaves.

He raked leaves for __2__ hours.

He already had __$26__.

2. What do you need to find?

How much money did Max earn raking leaves? How much money did Max have after he raked the leaves?

The problem has two questions. Answer the first one. Then, answer the second one.

Answer 3 to 6 to **plan and solve** the problem.

3. How can you answer the first question? __**Multiply 2 times 9.**__

4. Solve. How much did Max earn raking leaves? __**$18**__

5. How can you answer the second question? __**Add $26 and $18.**__

6. Solve. How much money did Max have after raking leaves? __**$44**__

Name ______________________

Math Diagnosis and Intervention System
Intervention Lesson E6

Two-Question Problems (continued)

Answer 7 to **check** your solution.

7. Reasoning Use an estimate to explain why your answer to how much money Max has now is reasonable.

Max earned about $20 raking leaves and he had about $30. $20 + $30 = $50. Since $44 is close to $50, $44 is reasonable.

Solve each problem. Answer both questions.

8. Ms. Olivia brought 7 bunches of bananas to the school picnic. Each bunch had 5 bananas. She also brought 27 apples.

How many bananas did she bring? __35__ bananas

How many more bananas than apples did Ms. Olivia bring? __8__ more

9. There are 3 children and 2 adults in Zac's family. Each person in the family donated $5 to charity.

How many people are in Zac's family? __5__ people

How much money did Zac's family donate to charity? __$25__

10. Monique read 45 pages on Saturday and 39 pages on Sunday. Her book has 113 pages.

How many pages did Monique read? __84__ pages

How many more pages does she need to read to finish her book? __29__ pages

11. Tandy bought 4 boxes of cat treats. Each box contains 2 packages. It takes 5 days to use each package of cat treats.

How many packages of cat treats did Tandy buy? __8__ packages

How many days worth of cat treats did Tandy buy? __40__ days

Teacher Notes

Ongoing Assessment

Ask: ***Can you answer the second question before the first one in most two-question problems?*** Sample answer: No; usually you need the answer to the first question to solve the second part of the problem.

Error Intervention

If students have trouble with the multiplication facts in the problem,

then use G25: Multiplying by 2 and 5 and G26: Multiplying by 9.

If You Have More Time

Have students write their own problem with two-questions and draw a picture to illustrate it. Have them explain how to solve the problem on the back of the page. Collect all the problems. If you started a problem solving book in intervention lesson E5, add these problems to it. Otherwise, bind the problems in a book titled "Our Problem Solving Book." When you have a few extra minutes, use the problems as a filler.

Multiple-Step Problems

Math Diagnosis and Intervention System
Intervention Lesson E7

Name ______________________

Multiple-Step Problems

At the sports store, Hannah bought 2 baseballs, and Jim bought 3 baseballs. The baseballs cost $6 each. How much did they spend?

Solve by answering 1 to 8.

Answer 1 and 2 to **understand** the problem.

1. What do you know from reading the problem?

Hannah bought 2 baseballs.

Jim bought 3 baseballs.

The baseballs cost $6 each.

2. What do you need to find?

How much did Hannah and Jim spend on the baseballs?

Answer 3 to 7 to **plan and solve** the problem.

3. How can you find how much Hannah and Jim spent?

Mulitply the number of baseballs they bought by $6.

4. Does the problem tell you how many baseballs Hannah and Jim bought altogether? no

5. Do you have enough information to find out how many baseballs Hannah and Jim bought altogether? yes

"How many baseballs did Hannah and Jim buy altogether?" is the **hidden question** in the problem. You need to answer the hidden question before you can solve the problem.

6. How many baseballs did Hannah and Jim buy altogether? 5

Math Diagnosis and Intervention System
Intervention Lesson E7

Name ______________________

Multiple-Step Problems (continued)

7. How much money did Hannah and Jim spend on the baseballs? $30

Answer 8 to **look back and check** your solution to the problem.

8. Did you answer the right question? yes

Write and answer the hidden question. Then solve the problem.

9. Henry had 571 baseball cards. He sold 395 of them. He then bought 275 new baseball cards. How many cards does he have now?

How many baseball cards did Henry have left after he sold 395 of them? 176 cards; 451 cards

Use the graph to answer Exercises 10 and 11.

Favorite Snack	
Fruit	☺ ☺ ☺
Sandwiches	☺ ☺
Cheese	☺
Pretzels	☺ ☺ ☺ ☺

Each ☺ = 3 votes.

10. How many students voted for fruit or cheese?

How many smiley faces are there for fruit and cheese? 4 smiley faces; 12 students

11. How many more students voted for pretzels than voted for sandwiches?

How many more smiley faces are there for pretzels than for sandwiches? 2 smiley faces; 6 students

12. It costs $3 to rent a DVD. Sue rented 4 DVDs and Fran rented 3 DVDs. How much did they pay in all?

How many DVDs did they rent in all? 7 DVDs; $21

13. Reasoning Describe another way to find how much Sue and Fran paid in all for the DVDs in Exercise 12.

Check that students use a different approach than used in Exercise 12. Sample answer: Find how much each spent and then add: $4 \times \$3 = \$12$, $3 \times \$3 = \$9$, and $\$12 + \$9 = \$21$.

Teacher Notes

Ongoing Assessment

Ask: ***Which type of problems are more difficult in general, two-step problems or two-question problems?*** Sample answer: Two-step problems are generally more difficult because you have to find the hidden question. You don't have to find the hidden question in two-question problems.

Error Intervention

If students have trouble with the multiplication facts in the problem,

then use some of the intervention lessons on basic multiplication facts, B47 to B55.

If You Have More Time

Have students write their own problem with multiple steps and draw a picture to illustrate it. Have them explain how to solve the problem on the back of the page, including writing and answering the hidden question. Collect all the problems. If you started a problem solving book in intervention lesson E5 or E6, add these problems to it. Otherwise, bind the problems in a book titled "Our Problem Solving Book." When you have a few extra minutes, use the problems as a filler.

Multiple-Step Problems

Math Diagnosis and Intervention System
Intervention Lesson E8

Name ______________________

Multiple-Step Problems

Melanie mixed 64 ounces of pineapple juice and 32 ounces of cherry juice to make a punch. She then poured all the punch into cups, with 8 ounces in each cup. How many cups of punch did Melanie pour?

Solve by answering 1 to 8.

Answer 1 and 2 to **understand** the problem.

1. What do you know from reading the problem?

   Melanie used **64 ounces** of pineapple juice.

   Melanie used **32 ounces** of cherry juice.

   Melanie poured **8 ounces** of punch into each cup.

2. What do you need to find?

   How many cups of punch did Melanie pour?

Answer 3 to 7 to **plan and solve** the problem.

3. How can you find how many cups of punch Melanie poured?

   Divide the total ounces of punch by 8.

4. Does the problem tell you how many ounces of punch Melanie made? **no**

5. Do you have enough information to find out how many ounces of punch Melanie made? **yes**

"How many ounces of punch did Melanie make?" is the **hidden question** in the problem. You need to answer the hidden question before you can solve the problem.

Intervention Lesson E8 49

Math Diagnosis and Intervention System
Intervention Lesson E8

Name ______________________

Multiple-Step Problems (continued)

6. How many ounces of punch did Melanie make? **96** ounces

7. How many cups of punch did Melanie pour? **12** cups

Answer 8 to **look back** at your solution to the problem.

8. **Reasoning** Describe another way to find how many cups of punch Melanie poured.

   Find how many 8-ounce cups of pineapple juice were in the punch and how many 8-ounce cups of cherry juice were in the punch. Then add the numbers of cups. $64 \div 8 = 8$ cups of pineapple juice; $32 \div 8 = 4$ cups of cherry juice. $8 + 4 = 12$ cups of punch.

Write and answer the hidden question. Then solve the problem.

9. Lacy bought 2 yards of blue material, 6 yards of red material, and 6 yards of white material, each for $2 a yard. How much change did she receive if she paid with a $50 bill?

   How many yards of material did Lacy buy in all? 14 yards; How much did the material cost in all? $28; $22 change

10. Trevor spent $34 on a video game at one store. Then at another store he spent a total of $38 on two model cars. How much more did the video game cost than one model car if each model car cost the same?

    How much did each model car cost? $19; $15 more

11. Elise ordered 5 pounds of hamburger packaged in freezer paper and the rest packaged for immediate use. Her total bill was $36. If each pound cost $4, how many pounds of hamburger was packaged for immediate use?

    How many pounds of hamburger did Elise buy in all? 9 pounds; 4 pounds

50 Intervention Lesson E8

Teacher Notes

Ongoing Assessment

Ask: ***In both multiple-step problems and problems with missing information, the problem does not give some of the information you need to solve. How can you tell the difference between these two types of problems?*** In multiple-step problems, information is provided that can be used to find the information needed to solve.

Error Intervention

If students have trouble dividing,

then use C51 or G54: Dividing Two-Digit Numbers.

If You Have More Time

Use markers and large letters to write the following, sentence on a different sheet of paper and give each sheet to a student.

Salvador's Sandwich Shop has 48 ounces of turkey. Salvador's Sandwich Shop has 38 ounces of beef. Salvador uses 6 ounces of meat on each sandwich. How many sandwiches can the shop make?

Ask the students to come to the front of the class. Give another student a blank sheet of paper and a marker and ask him or her to write the hidden question. Have the students who are still sitting answer the hidden question and solve the problem. Discuss the solution as a class. Then, give two more students blank sheets of paper and markers. Have them work together to write two hidden questions (one each) which together can be used to solve the problem. Have the class answer the hidden questions and solve the problem again. Discuss how there is usually more than one way to solve a problem. One hidden question is: How many ounces of meat does the shop have? (84) The other set is: How many turkey sandwiches can the shop make? (8) How many beef sandwiches can the shop make? (6) The shop can make 14 sandwiches.

Look for a Pattern

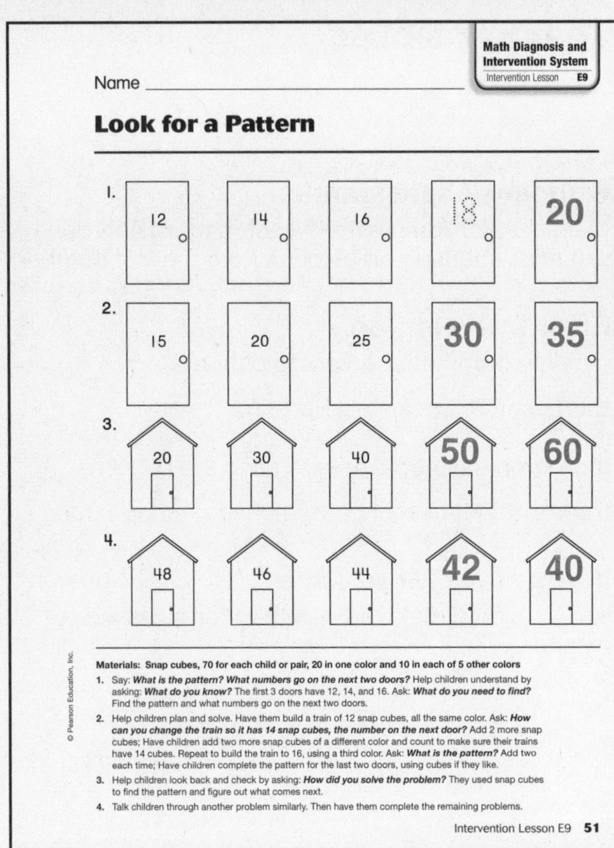
Math Diagnosis and Intervention System
Intervention Lesson E9

Name ______________________

Look for a Pattern

1. 12, 14, 16, 18, 20

2. 15, 20, 25, 30, 35

3. 20, 30, 40, 50, 60

4. 48, 46, 44, 42, 40

Materials: Snap cubes, 70 for each child or pair, 20 in one color and 10 in each of 5 other colors

1. Say: ***What is the pattern? What numbers go on the next two doors?*** Help children understand by asking: ***What do you know?*** The first 3 doors have 12, 14, and 16. Ask: ***What do you need to find?*** Find the pattern and what numbers go on the next two doors.
2. Help children plan and solve. Have them build a train of 12 snap cubes, all the same color. Ask: ***How can you change the train so it has 14 snap cubes, the number on the next door?*** Add 2 more snap cubes; Have children add two more snap cubes of a different color and count to make sure their trains have 14 cubes. Repeat to build the train to 16, using a third color. Ask: ***What is the pattern?*** Add two each time; Have children complete the pattern for the last two doors, using cubes if they like.
3. Help children look back and check by asking: ***How did you solve the problem?*** They used snap cubes to find the pattern and figure out what comes next.
4. Talk children through another problem similarly. Then have them complete the remaining problems.

© Pearson Education, Inc.

Intervention Lesson E9 **51**

Teacher Notes

Ongoing Assessment

Observe which children use cubes in the Exercises and which use skip counting.

Error Intervention

If children have trouble counting to complete the patterns,

then use A7: Counting by 10s to 100 and A8: Counting to 100.

If You Have More Time

Have children draw and color a picture of 5 objects in a row with a number pattern other than houses or doors.

Math Diagnosis and Intervention System
Intervention Lesson E9

Name ______________________

Look for a Pattern (continued)

Look for the pattern.
Write the missing numbers.

5. 4, 6, 8, 10, 12

6. 40, 35, 30, 25, 20

7. 28, 30, 32, 34, 36

8. 70, 60, 50, 40, 30

9. **Reasoning** Make your own pattern. **Check patterns.**
30

© Pearson Education, Inc.

52 Intervention Lesson E9

Look for a Pattern

Name ____________________

Look for a Pattern

1. Jana is making a necklace with two colors of beads. She uses 1 red bead, then 3 blue beads, then 5 yellow beads. If she continues this pattern with green and then orange beads, how many orange beads will she use?

1, 3, 5, 7, 9

Pattern: Each new color has 2 more beads.

2. Mario had 4 football cards to start. The table shows how many he had after buying new packs. How many cards did he have after buying 5 packs?

Packs	Cards
1 pack	14
2 packs	24
3 packs	34
4 packs	44
5 packs	54

Pattern: Mario got 10 more cards in each pack.

Materials: Crayons or markers

1. Read the problem to the children. Help them understand by asking: ***What do you know?*** Jana uses 1 red, then 3 blue, and then 5 yellow beads to make a necklace. Have children color the picture of the necklace to match the information in the problem. ***What else do you know?*** Jana will use green beads next and then orange beads. ***What do you need to find?*** Find how many orange beads she will use.
2. Help children plan and solve by asking: ***How many green beads will Jana use?*** Have children write 7. ***What color will Jana use after green?*** orange; ***How many orange beads will Jana use?*** Have children write 9.
3. Help children look back and check by asking: ***Did you answer the right question?*** Yes, Jana will use 9 orange beads. Ask: ***What is the pattern?*** Each new color uses two more beads. Have children write the pattern.
4. Do the other problem similarly.

Name ____________________

Look for a Pattern (continued)

Find the pattern.
Write the missing numbers.

3. Ana's scarf has 2 parts yellow, then 5 parts green, then 8 parts orange. If it continues this pattern with white and then brown parts, how many brown parts does it have?

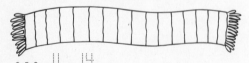

2, 5, 8, 11, 14

Pattern: Each new color has 3 more parts.

4. The table shows how many placemats children made each day at camp. If the pattern continued, how many placemats did they make on Friday?

Day	Placemats
Monday	6
Tuesday	16
Wednesday	26
Thursday	36
Friday	46

Pattern: 10 more placemats each day.

What comes next in each pattern?

5. 5, 9, 13, 17, 21
6. 4, 6, 8, 10, 12
7. 13, 23, 33, 43, 53
8. 26, 31, 36, 41, 46

Teacher Notes

Ongoing Assessment

Make sure children extend each pattern and don't just start counting on by ones from the last number.

Error Intervention

If children do not understand patterns,

then use E9: Look for a Pattern.

If children have trouble extending the patterns,

then let them use a hundred chart or snap cubes.

If You Have More Time

Have children make up a pattern for a partner to extend.

Make a Table and Look for a Pattern

Name ____________________

Make a Table and Look for a Pattern

1. There are 5 bicycles in the yard.
Each bicycle has 2 wheels.
How many wheels are there in the yard altogether?

Number of Bicycles	1	2	3	4	5
Number of Wheels	2	4	6	8	10

There are 10 wheels in the yard altogether.

2. There are 4 boxes. Each box has 5 pencils.
How many pencils are there in all?

Number of Boxes	1	2	3	4
Number of Pencils	5	10	15	20

There are 20 pencils in all.

3. There are 3 monkeys.
Each monkey has 10 toes.
How many toes are there in all?

Number of Monkeys	1	2	3
Number of Toes	10	20	30

There are 30 toes in all.

Materials: Snap cubes, 20 for each child

1. Read the problem to the children. Help them understand by asking: ***What do you know?*** There are 5 bicycles in the yard. Each bicycle has 2 wheels. ***What do you need to find?*** Find how many wheels there are in the yard altogether.
2. Help children plan and solve. Say: ***You can solve the problem by making a table to show a pattern. How many wheels does 1 bicycle have?*** 2 ***How many wheels do 2 bicycles have?*** 4 ***How many wheels do 3 bicycles have?*** 6. Then, have them complete the table, using snap cubes if necessary. Ask: ***How many wheels are there in the yard altogether?*** 10
3. Help children look back by asking: ***What was the pattern?*** Sample answer: Add two more wheels for each bicycle.
4. Do the other problems similarly.

Name ____________________

Make a Table and Look for a Pattern (continued)

Find the pattern. Write the numbers.

4. There are 5 sheep. Each sheep gives 3 bags of wool. How many bags of wool in all?

Number of Sheep	1	2	3	4	5
Number of Bags	3	6	9	12	15

There are 15 bags of wool in all.

5. There are 4 cats. Each cat has 4 paws. How many paws in all?

Number of Cats	1	2	3	4
Number of Paws	4	8	12	16

The cats have 16 paws in all.

6. **Reasoning** If there are 5 cats, how many paws do they have altogether? 20 paws

Teacher Notes

Ongoing Assessment

Observe whether children complete the tables by rows or by columns. If they complete them by rows, they might be looking at the pattern in each row, rather than associating inputs and outputs. Ask children who are completing tables by row questions such as: ***How many bags of wool are there for 4 sheep?***

Error Intervention

If children have trouble finding the numbers in the second row of each table,

then A7: Counting by 10s to 100 and A16: Using Skip Counting.

If You Have More Time

Have children create their own tables to show a pattern.

Make a Table

Math Diagnosis and Intervention System
Intervention Lesson E12

Name ______________________

Make a Table

1. How many different ways can Carlos put 4 balls in 2 boxes?

Box 1	Box 2
4	0
3	1
2	2
1	3
0	4

There are __5__ ways.

2. How many different ways can Trina put 5 balls in 2 boxes?

Box 1	Box 2
5	0
4	1
3	2
2	3
1	4
0	5

There are __6__ ways.

Materials: Two half sheets of paper and 10 counters for each child

1. Read the problem and help children understand by asking: ***What do you know?*** Carlos wants to put 4 balls into 2 boxes. ***What do you need to find?*** Find how many ways Carlos can put 4 balls into 2 boxes.
2. Help children plan and solve by saying: ***You can solve the problem by making a table.*** Have children put 4 counters on one sheet of paper and ask: ***What is one way Carlos can put 4 balls in 2 boxes?*** Have children trace 4 and 0 in the table. Then, have them move one counter to the other sheet of paper and ask: ***What is another way Carlos can put 4 balls in 2 boxes?*** Have children trace 3 and write 1 in the table. Continue until children complete the table, moving one counter at a time. Ask: ***How many ways can Carlos put 4 balls into 2 boxes?*** Have children write 5.
3. Help children look back and check by asking: ***How do we know we have all the possible ways?*** The first box can only have 4, 3, 2, 1, or 0 balls. Do the other problem similarly.

Intervention Lesson E12 **57**

Math Diagnosis and Intervention System
Intervention Lesson E12

Name ______________________

Make a Table (continued)

3. Latisha wants to give 3 bottles of juice to her friends. How many different choices of juice does Latisha have?
Fill in the table to solve the problem.

Apple Juice	Grape Juice	Orange Juice
3	0	0
2	1	0
2	0	1
1	2	0
1	1	1
1	0	2
0	3	0
0	2	1
0	1	2
0	0	3

Latisha has __10__ choices.

58 Intervention Lesson E12

Teacher Notes

Ongoing Assessment

Ask: ***There are 5 ways Carlos can put 4 balls in the boxes and 6 ways Trina can put 5 balls in the boxes. How many ways do you think Misty can put 7 balls in two boxes?*** 8 ways

Error Intervention

If children have trouble solving the juice problem,

then encourage them to use three sheets of paper and let each sheet represent a type of juice.

If You Have More Time

Have children make a table to list how many ways Coach Rogers can put 10 balls in 2 boxes. There are 11 ways.

Use Objects

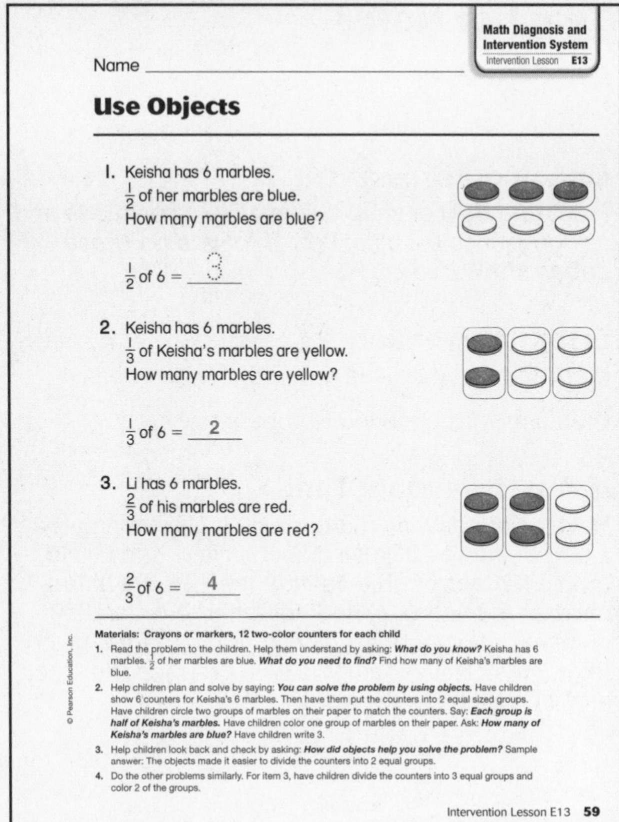

Math Diagnosis and Intervention System
Intervention Lesson E13

Name ______________________

Use Objects

1. Keisha has 6 marbles.
$\frac{1}{2}$ of her marbles are blue.
How many marbles are blue?

$\frac{1}{2}$ of 6 = 3

2. Keisha has 6 marbles.
$\frac{1}{3}$ of Keisha's marbles are yellow.
How many marbles are yellow?

$\frac{1}{3}$ of 6 = 2

3. Li has 6 marbles.
$\frac{2}{3}$ of his marbles are red.
How many marbles are red?

$\frac{2}{3}$ of 6 = 4

Materials: Crayons or markers, 12 two-color counters for each child

1. Read the problem to the children. Help them understand by asking: ***What do you know?*** Keisha has 6 marbles. $\frac{1}{2}$ of her marbles are blue. ***What do you need to find?*** Find how many of Keisha's marbles are blue.
2. Help children plan and solve by saying: ***You can solve the problem by using objects.*** Have children show 6 counters for Keisha's 6 marbles. Then have them put the counters into 2 equal sized groups. Have children circle two groups of marbles on their paper to match the counters. Say: ***Each group is half of Keisha's marbles.*** Have children color one group of marbles on their paper. Ask: ***How many of Keisha's marbles are blue?*** Have children write 3.
3. Help children look back and check by asking: ***How did objects help you solve the problem?*** Sample answer: The objects made it easier to divide the counters into 2 equal groups.
4. Do the other problems similarly. For item 3, have children divide the counters into 3 equal groups and color 2 of the groups.

Intervention Lesson E13 **59**

Math Diagnosis and Intervention System
Intervention Lesson E13

Name ______________________

Use Objects (continued)

Use counters to solve.

4. Jim has 8 apples.
$\frac{1}{2}$ of his apples are red.
How many of Jim's apples are red?

$\frac{1}{2}$ of 8 = 4

5. Lisa has 8 apples.
$\frac{3}{4}$ of her apples are red.
How many of Lisa's apples are red?

$\frac{3}{4}$ of 8 = 6

6. Vero has 9 apples.
$\frac{2}{3}$ of her apples are red.
How many of Vero's apples are red?

$\frac{2}{3}$ of 9 = 6

7. Al has 12 apples.
$\frac{1}{4}$ of his apples are red.
How many of Al's apples are red?

$\frac{1}{4}$ of 12 = 3

60 Intervention Lesson E13

Teacher Notes

Ongoing Assessment

Observe which children use counters in the Exercises and which can solve from the pictures.

Error Intervention

If children have trouble with the fraction concepts,

then use A37: Fractions of a Set and A39: Writing Fractions for Part of a Set.

If You Have More Time

Have 12 children come to the front of the room. Have the children who are still sitting take turns telling them how to make groups to find each part of 12: $\frac{1}{2}$ [6], $\frac{1}{4}$ [3], $\frac{1}{3}$ [4], $\frac{3}{4}$ [9], and $\frac{2}{3}$ [8].

Act It Out

Math Diagnosis and Intervention System
Intervention Lesson E14

Name ______________________

Act It Out

1. Sue has 5 bells.
Tim has 6 bells.
Caro has 3 bells.

3	5	6
least	between	most

Who has the most bells? Tim

Who has the least bells? Caro

2. Will has 8 toy cars.
Joe has 5 toy cars.
Patty has 7 toy cars.

5	7	8
least	between	most

Who has the most toy cars? Will

Who has the least toy cars? Joe

Materials: Snap cubes, 21 for each child

1. Read the problem to the children. Help them understand by asking: ***What do you know?*** Sue has 5 bells. Tim has 6 bells. Caro has 3 bells. ***What do you need to find?*** Find who has the most bells and who has the least.
2. Help children plan and solve by saying: ***You can solve the problem by acting out the problem with snap cubes.*** Have children make a train of 5 snap cubes for Sue's bells, a train of 6 snap cubes for Tim's bell, and a train of 3 snap cubes for Caro's bells.
3. Have children arrange the trains in order from the one with the least snap cubes to the one with the most. Ask: ***How many cubes are in the train with the least?*** Have children trace 3 above the line with least. Ask: ***How many cubes are in the train with the most?*** Have children trace 6 above the line with most. ***How many cubes are in the train that is between 3 and 6?*** Have children trace 5 above the line with between. Say: ***Six was the most. Who had 6 bells?*** Have children trace Tim. ***Three was the least. Who had 3 bells?*** Have children write Caro.
4. Help children look back and check by saying: ***Did you answer the right question?*** yes
5. Do the other problem similarly.

Math Diagnosis and Intervention System
Intervention Lesson E14

Name ______________________

Act It Out (continued)

Use the cubes to act out the story.
Write the numbers from least to greatest.
Answer the questions.

Some children collect leaves.

3. Ana has 6 leaves.
Jay has 9 leaves.
Tom has 5 leaves.

5	6	9
least	between	most

Who has the most leaves? Jay

Who has the least leaves? Tom

4. Kay has 7 leaves.
Mark has 4 leaves.
Lee has 10 leaves.

4	7	10
least	between	most

Who has the most leaves? Lee

Who has the least leaves? Mark

5. Min has 3 leaves.
Wendy has 8 leaves.
Patty has 6 leaves.

3	6	8
least	between	most

Who has the most leaves? Wendy

Who has the least leaves? Min

Teacher Notes

Ongoing Assessment

Point to a train of snap cubes a child has made and ask questions such as: ***Who's leaves do these cubes show?***

Error Intervention

If children have trouble ordering the numbers,

then use A12: Ordering Numbers to 12.

If You Have More Time

Have children work in groups of 3. Give each group a bag of about 20 small objects. Have each child grab a handful of objects from the bag. Have the children in the group work together to order the numbers of objects each child grabbed from least to greatest. Have them find who grabbed the most and who grabbed the least.

Make an Organized List

Name ______________________

Make an Organized List

1. Find 4 ways you can make this shape using pattern blocks.

These are the same way.

Ways to Make			
Shapes I used			
Way 1	1	0	1
Way 2	0	2	0
Way 3	0	1	2
Way 4	0	0	4

Materials: Pattern blocks, including 1 hexagon, 2 trapezoids, 1 parallelogram, 3 rhombuses, and 6 triangles for each pair, or group

1. Read the problem to the children. Help them understand by asking: ***What do you need to find?*** Find 3 different ways to make the pattern block shown using other pattern blocks. Show children how to put the trapezoid and triangle on top of the parallelogram block. Tell them this is one way to make the block. Then, have children turn the blocks (not pick them up and rearrange them) so they look like the other combination shown above. Ask: ***Are these the same way to show the block or is this a different way?*** It is the same way.
2. Help children plan and solve by saying: ***You can solve by making an organized list. You made the block using one of these*** (hold up trapezoid) ***and one of these*** (hold up triangle)***, so put a 1 under each of these shapes in the list.*** Have children trace the 1, 0, and 1 in the first row of the table.
3. Have children work together to find 3 other ways to make the shape and complete the table.
4. Help children look back and check by saying: ***Did you find 4 different ways?*** Discuss the ways the children found and how they recorded the ways in the table.

Name ______________________

Make an Organized List (continued)

2. Use pattern blocks. How many ways can you make this shape? Record the blocks you used.

Ways to Make				
Shapes I used				
Way 1	1	0	0	0
Way 2	0	1	0	3
Way 3	0	1	1	1
Way 4	0	2	0	0
Way 5	0	0	1	4
Way 6	0	0	2	2
Way 7	0	0	3	0
Way 8	0	0	0	6

How many ways can you make a hexagon? 8

Teacher Notes

Ongoing Assessment

Observe to see which children organize their list and which just find ways in an unorganized manner. Encourage children to find all ways with trapezoids before finding a way without one.

Error Intervention

If children have trouble combining pattern blocks,

then use D52: Making New Shapes from Shapes.

If You Have More Time

Give children coins and have them make an organized list to find all the ways to make 35 cents with dimes, nickels, and pennies. There are 19 ways.

Try, Check, and Revise

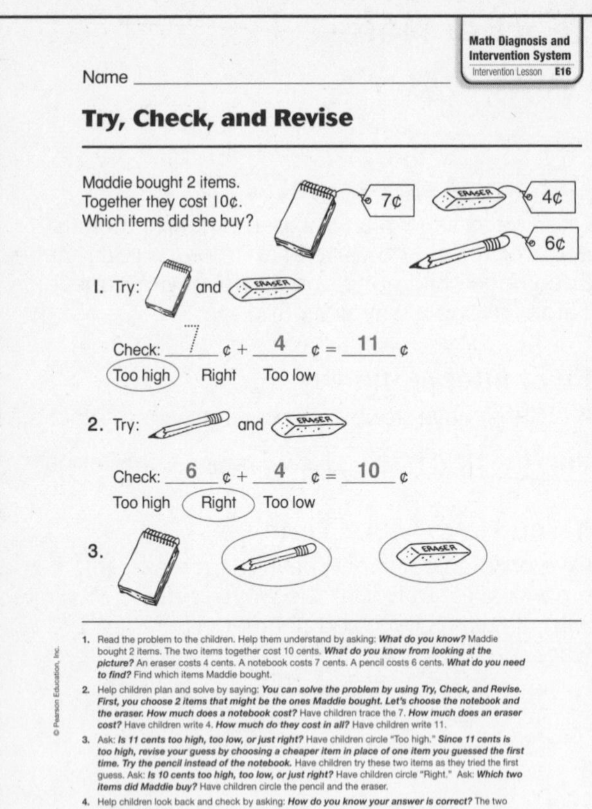
Math Diagnosis and Intervention System
Intervention Lesson E16

Name ______________________________

Try, Check, and Revise

Maddie bought 2 items.
Together they cost 10¢.
Which items did she buy?

1. Try: [notebook] and [eraser]

   Check: 7 ¢ + 4 ¢ = 11 ¢
   (Too high) Right Too low

2. Try: [pencil] and [eraser]

   Check: 6 ¢ + 4 ¢ = 10 ¢
   Too high (Right) Too low

3. [notebook] (pencil) (eraser)

1. Read the problem to the children. Help them understand by asking: ***What do you know?*** Maddie bought 2 items. The two items together cost 10 cents. ***What do you know from looking at the picture?*** An eraser costs 4 cents. A notebook costs 7 cents. A pencil costs 6 cents. ***What do you need to find?*** Find which items Maddie bought.
2. Help children plan and solve by saying: ***You can solve the problem by using Try, Check, and Revise. First, you choose 2 items that might be the ones Maddie bought. Let's choose the notebook and the eraser. How much does a notebook cost?*** Have children trace the 7. ***How much does an eraser cost?*** Have children write 4. ***How much do they cost in all?*** Have children write 11.
3. Ask: ***Is 11 cents too high, too low, or just right?*** Have children circle "Too high." ***Since 11 cents is too high, revise your guess by choosing a cheaper item in place of one item you guessed the first time. Try the pencil instead of the notebook.*** Have children try these two items as they tried the first guess. Ask: ***Is 10 cents too high, too low, or just right?*** Have children circle "Right." Ask: ***Which two items did Maddie buy?*** Have children circle the pencil and the eraser.
4. Help children look back and check by asking: ***How do you know your answer is correct?*** The two items cost 10 cents.

Intervention Lesson E16 **65**

Teacher Notes

Ongoing Assessment

Observe which children understand the logic of guessing a cheaper item when the first total is too high or guessing a more expensive item when the first guess is too low. Children who do not understand will need more guesses to find the answer.

Error Intervention

If children have trouble finding the total costs,

then let them use pennies.

If You Have More Time

Have children work in pairs. Let them put price tags on 3 or 4 objects and make up problems like the ones in the lesson. Have them trade problems and solve.

Math Diagnosis and Intervention System
Intervention Lesson **E16**

Name ______________________________

Try, Check, and Revise (continued)

Guess which toys each child bought.
Write a number sentence to check your guess.
Try again until you find the right toys.
Circle the toys each child bought.

[car] 7¢ 6¢ [ring] [mask] 9¢ 5¢ [top]

4. Javier bought 2 different toys.
   Together they cost 11¢ **Guesses will vary.**

   Try: ____ ¢ + ____ ¢ = ____ ¢
   Try: ____ ¢ + ____ ¢ = ____ ¢
   Try: 6 ¢ + 5 ¢ = 11 ¢

5. May-Li bought 2 different toys.
   Together they cost 16¢

   Try: ____ ¢ + ____ ¢ = ____ ¢
   Try: ____ ¢ + ____ ¢ = ____ ¢
   Try: 7 ¢ + 9 ¢ = 16 ¢

66 Intervention Lesson E16

Use Objects and Reasoning

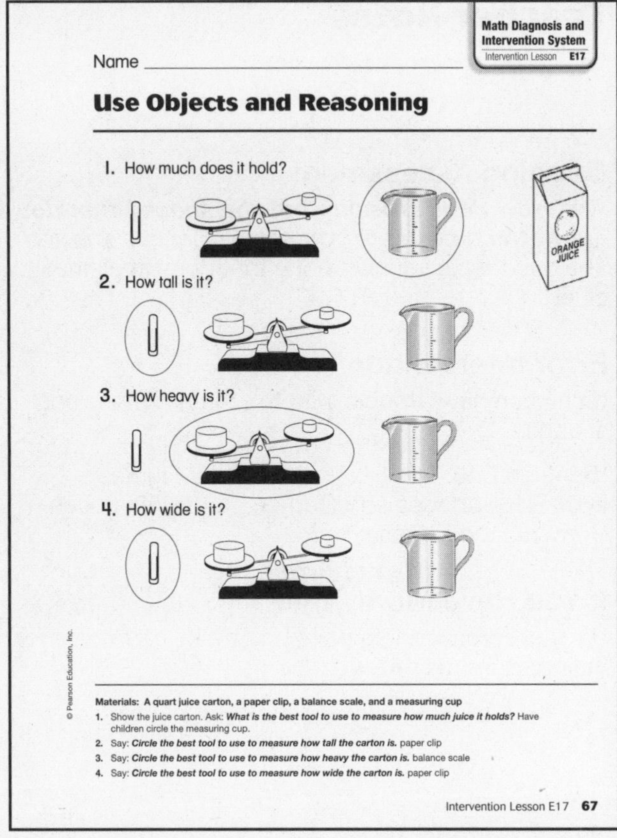

Math Diagnosis and Intervention System
Intervention Lesson E17

Name ____________________

Use Objects and Reasoning

1. How much does it hold?

2. How tall is it?

3. How heavy is it?

4. How wide is it?

Materials: A quart juice carton, a paper clip, a balance scale, and a measuring cup

1. Show the juice carton. Ask: ***What is the best tool to use to measure how much juice it holds?*** Have children circle the measuring cup.
2. Say: ***Circle the best tool to use to measure how tall the carton is.*** paper clip
3. Say: ***Circle the best tool to use to measure how heavy the carton is.*** balance scale
4. Say: ***Circle the best tool to use to measure how wide the carton is.*** paper clip

Intervention Lesson E17 **67**

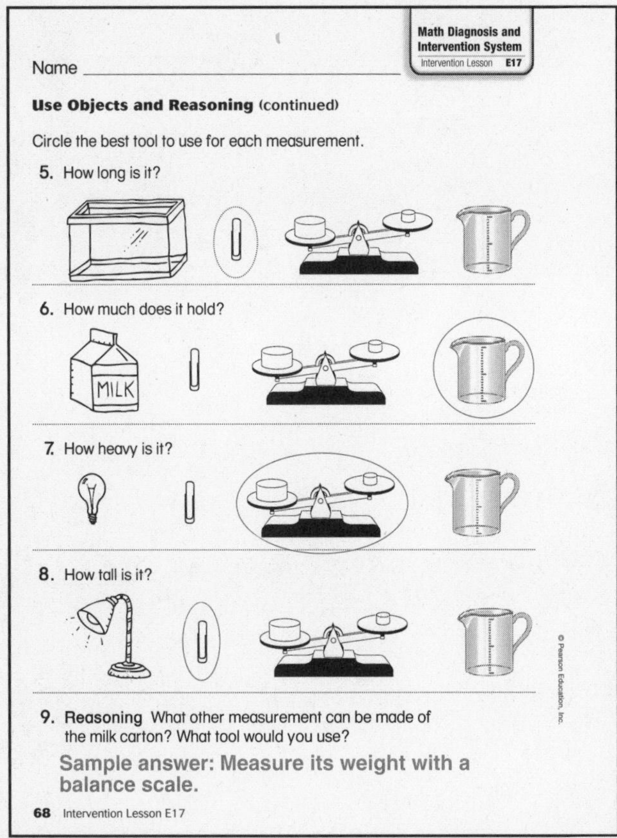

Math Diagnosis and Intervention System
Intervention Lesson E17

Name ____________________

Use Objects and Reasoning (continued)

Circle the best tool to use for each measurement.

5. How long is it?

6. How much does it hold?

7. How heavy is it?

8. How tall is it?

9. **Reasoning** What other measurement can be made of the milk carton? What tool would you use?

Sample answer: Measure its weight with a balance scale.

68 Intervention Lesson E17

Teacher Notes

Ongoing Assessment

Observe to see which children realize the object is not important in deciding what tool to use, but the importance is on the question. For example, if the question asks how heavy an object is, use the balance scale

Error Intervention

If children do not understand measuring length, capacity, or weight,

then use D22: Unit Size and Measuring, D28: Exploring Capacity, and D31: Estimating and Measuring Weight.

If You Have More Time

Have children estimate and measure the length, weight, or capacity of several objects.

Use Reasoning

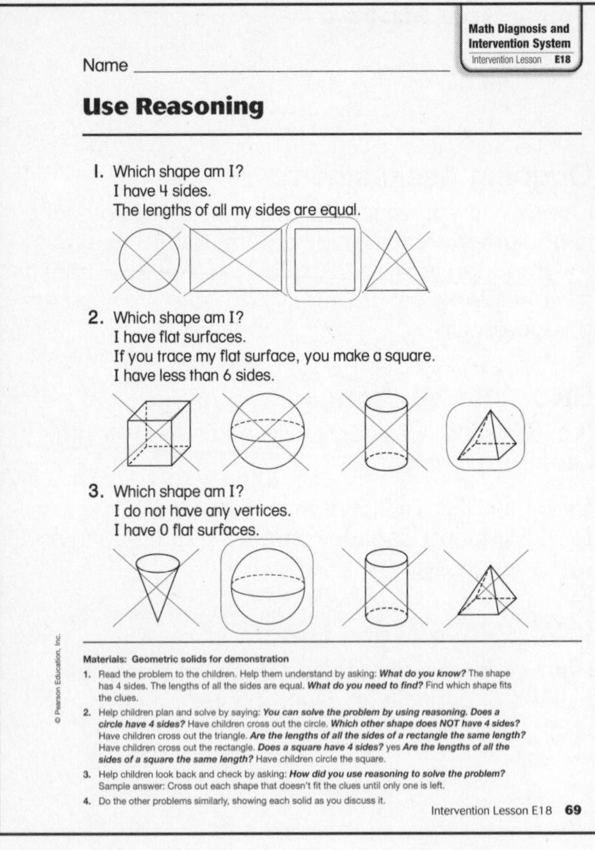

Math Diagnosis and Intervention System
Intervention Lesson E18

Name ______________________________

Use Reasoning

1. Which shape am I?
I have 4 sides.
The lengths of all my sides are equal.

2. Which shape am I?
I have flat surfaces.
If you trace my flat surface, you make a square.
I have less than 6 sides.

3. Which shape am I?
I do not have any vertices.
I have 0 flat surfaces.

Materials: Geometric solids for demonstration

1. Read the problem to the children. Help them understand by asking: ***What do you know?*** The shape has 4 sides. The lengths of all the sides are equal. ***What do you need to find?*** Find which shape fits the clues.
2. Help children plan and solve by saying: ***You can solve the problem by using reasoning. Does a circle have 4 sides?*** Have children cross out the circle. ***Which other shape does NOT have 4 sides?*** Have children cross out the triangle. ***Are the lengths of all the sides of a rectangle the same length?*** Have children cross out the rectangle. ***Does a square have 4 sides?*** yes ***Are the lengths of all the sides of a square the same length?*** Have children circle the square.
3. Help children look back and check by asking: ***How did you use reasoning to solve the problem?*** Sample answer: Cross out each shape that doesn't fit the clues until only one is left.
4. Do the other problems similarly, showing each solid as you discuss it.

© Pearson Education, Inc.

Intervention Lesson E18 **69**

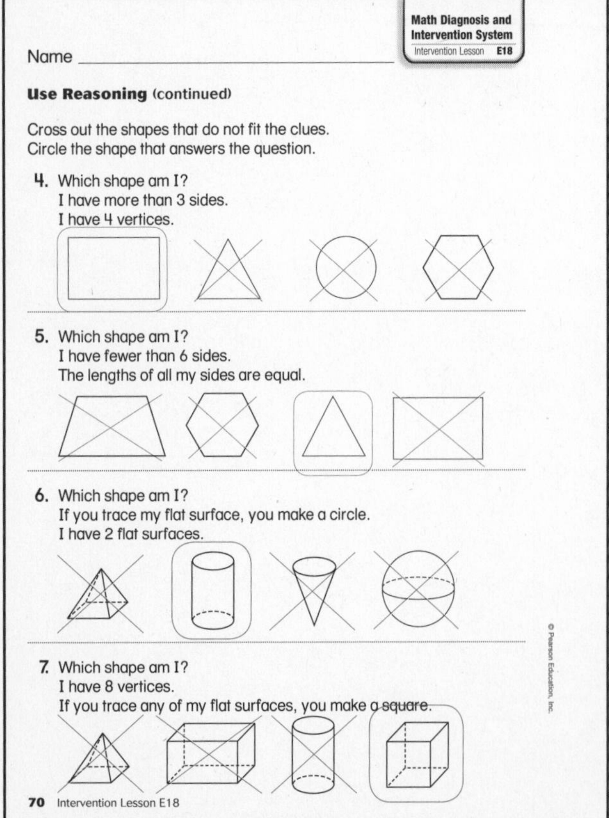

Math Diagnosis and Intervention System
Intervention Lesson E18

Name ______________________________

Use Reasoning (continued)

Cross out the shapes that do not fit the clues.
Circle the shape that answers the question.

4. Which shape am I?
I have more than 3 sides.
I have 4 vertices.

5. Which shape am I?
I have fewer than 6 sides.
The lengths of all my sides are equal.

6. Which shape am I?
If you trace my flat surface, you make a circle.
I have 2 flat surfaces.

7. Which shape am I?
I have 8 vertices.
If you trace any of my flat surfaces, you make a square.

© Pearson Education, Inc.

70 Intervention Lesson E18

Teacher Notes

Ongoing Assessment

Ask: ***How does crossing out the shapes that do not fit the clues help you solve?*** Sample answer: The one that is left is the one that does fit all the clues.

Error Intervention

If children have trouble with the three-dimensional shapes,

then use D50: Flat Surfaces of Solid Figures, D57: Flat Surfaces and Corners, and D58: Faces, Corners, and Edges.

If You Have More Time

Have children work in pairs and make up riddles for their partner to solve.

Draw a Picture and Write a Number Sentence

Name ______________________________

Draw a Picture and Write a Number Sentence

1. Rico has 5 stickers.
He gets 2 more stickers.
How many stickers does he have in all?

5 (+) 2 = 7

7 stickers in all

2. Maria has 6 stickers.
She gives 3 stickers to Dani.
How many stickers does Maria have left?

6 (−) 3 = 3

3 stickers left

1. Read the problem to the children. Help them understand by asking: ***What do you know?*** Rico has 5 stickers. Rico gets 2 more stickers. ***What do you need to find?*** Find how many stickers Rico has in all.
2. Help children plan and solve by saying: ***You can solve the problem by drawing a picture and writing a number sentence. To find how many stickers Rico has in all, do you need to add or subtract?*** Have children write a plus sign in the circle. Ask: ***What do you need to add?*** Have children trace 5 and 2. Have children draw a picture of circles to show the problem and to find 5 + 2. Ask: ***What is 5 plus 2?*** Have children write 7. ***How many stickers does Rico have in all?*** Have children write 7.
3. Help children look back and check by asking: ***What is your number sentence?*** 5 + 2 = 7
4. Do the other problem similarly. Have children draw circles and then cross them out for the picture.

Name ______________________________

Draw a Picture and Write a Number Sentence (continued)

Write a number sentence.
Draw a picture and solve.

3. Marcia made 7 bracelets.
She gave 3 bracelets to her friends.
How many bracelets does she have left.

7 (−) 3 (=) 4 — 4 bracelets

4. The red team won 12 games.
The white team won 8 games.
How many more games did the red team win?

12 (−) 8 (=) 4 — 4 games

Use the table to help you solve Exercises 5 and 6.

Players	Game 1	Game 2
Harvey	5	7
Juanita	8	4

5. How many points did Harvey score altogether in Games 1 and 2?

5 (+) 7 (=) 12 points

6. How many more points did Juanita score in Game 1 than Harvey?

8 (−) 5 (=) 3 points

Teacher Notes

Ongoing Assessment

See if children's pictures reflect the problem, especially subtraction as separating verses comparison.

Error Intervention

If children have trouble with the addition and subtraction concepts,

then use B7: Joining Stories, B17: Separating Stories, B18: Comparing Stories, B25: Stories about Joining, B32: Stories about Separating, and B33: Stories about Comparing.

If You Have More Time

Have children write a problem. Then have them draw a picture that represents the problem, write a number sentence, and solve. Encourage children to draw pictures of objects in the problem, instead of circles. Let them color their pictures. Display their work.

Draw a Picture and Write a Number Sentence

Math Diagnosis and Intervention System
Intervention Lesson E20

Name ______________________

Draw a Picture and Write a Number Sentence

1. How many apples in all?

15

3 × 5 = 15

2. How many cherries in all?

12

3 × 4 = 12

1. Read the problem to the children. Help them understand by asking: ***What do you know?*** There are 3 baskets. There are 5 apples in each basket ***What do you need to find?*** Find how many apples in all.
2. Help children plan and solve by saying: ***You can solve by drawing a picture and writing a number sentence. Are all the groups the same size?*** yes; Have children draw circles in the model to show the 3 groups of 5. ***Since all the groups are the same size, you can multiply. How many groups are there?*** Have children trace 3. ***How many are in each group?*** Have children trace 5. ***How many apples in all?*** Have children write 15 in the number sentence and in the model.
3. Help children look back and check by asking: ***What is your number sentence?*** 3 × 5 = 15
4. Do the other problem similarly, asking how many rows and how many in each row.

Intervention Lesson E20 **73**

Math Diagnosis and Intervention System
Intervention Lesson E20

Name ______________________

Draw a Picture and Write a Number Sentence (continued)

Draw a picture and write a number sentence.
Solve.

3. How many bananas in all?

10

2 × 5 = 10

4. How many shells in all?

12

4 × 3 = 12

5. How many stars in all?

12

2 × 6 = 12

74 Intervention Lesson E20

Teacher Notes

Ongoing Assessment

Ask: ***How do you know when you can multiply instead of add?*** All the groups must be the same size before you can multiply.

Error Intervention

If children have trouble finding how many in all,

then let them use counters.

If You Have More Time

Have children write a multiplication problem. Have them draw and color a picture to go with it. Then have them draw a model, write a number sentence, and solve. Display their work.

Make a Table and Look for a Pattern

Math Diagnosis and Intervention System
Intervention Lesson E21

Name ____________________

Make a Table and Look for a Pattern

Ann and Jane began reading the same book on the same day. If Ann reads 8 pages each day and Jane reads 5 pages each day, what page will Jane read on the day that Ann reads page 40?

Solve by answering 1 to 6.

Answer 1 and 2 to **understand** the problem.

1. What do you know from reading the problem?

Ann reads __8__ pages each day.

Jane reads __5__ pages each day.

They started the same day.

2. What do you need to find?

What page will Jane read on the day Ann reads page 40?

Answer 3 to 5 to **plan and solve** the problem.

You can solve the problem by making a table and looking for a pattern.

3. Use patterns to complete the table below.

Day	1	2	3	4	5	6
Ann's Page	8	16	24	32	40	48
Jane's Page	5	10	15	20	25	30

4. What day will Ann read page 40? __day 5__

5. What page will Jane read on the day Ann reads page 40? __page 25__

Math Diagnosis and Intervention System
Intervention Lesson E21

Name ____________________

Make a Table and Look for a Pattern (continued)

Answer 6 to **look back** at your solution.

6. Did you answer the right question? __yes__

Use patterns to complete each table. Solve each problem.

7. Rebecca must put 4 eggs in each basket. There are 8 baskets. How many eggs does she need? __32 eggs__

Number of Baskets	1	2	3	4	5	6	7	8
Number of Eggs	4	8	12	16	20	24	28	32

8. Martin needs to water each tree with 3 gallons of water. How many gallons of water will he need for 7 trees?

Number of trees	1	2	3	4	5	6	7
Gallons of water	3	6	9	12	15	18	21

Martin will need 21 gallons of water.

9. Diego recorded the height of a bean plant. The first week, the plant was 2 inches high. The second, third, and fourth week, it was 4 inches, 6 inches, and 8 inches high. At this rate, when will the bean plant be 12 inches high?

Week	1	2	3	4	5	6	7
Height	2	4	6	8	10	12	14

The bean plant will be 12 inches high in 6 weeks.

10. Each quilt square has 2 red sections and 3 blue sections. If 18 blue sections are used, how many red sections are needed?

squares	1	2	3	4	5	6
red sections	2	4	6	8	10	12
blue sections	3	6	9	12	15	18

12 red sections

Teacher Notes

Ongoing Assessment

Ask students how they extended the pattern in each table. Notice which students used multiplication, which used skip counting, and which used addition.

Error Intervention

If students have trouble understanding the problems in the exercises,

then ask questions like "What do you know from reading the problem?" and "What do you need to find?"

If You Have More Time

Have students work in pairs. One student writes a rule for a pattern on a piece of paper, but does not let the partner see it. The partner must guess the rule by saying inputs. The first student says the output for each input. The second student records the inputs and outputs in a table until he or she can guess the rule. Then, have students change roles and repeat.

Act It Out

Name ______________________

Act It Out

Materials color tiles, 16 for each student

Jada bought balloons for the party. She bought red, yellow, and blue balloons. She bought at least one of each color. Use the information at the right to find how many balloons of each color she bought.

Balloons Jada Bought
7 yellow
3 more red than blue
16 balloons in all

Solve by answering 1 to 6.

Answer 1 to 3 to **understand** the problem.

1. What do you know from reading the problem?

Jada bought __red__, __yellow__, and __blue__ balloons.

2. What do you know from reading the chart?

Jada bought __7__ yellow balloons.

Jada bought __3__ more red balloons than blue balloons.

Jada bought __16__ balloons in all.

3. What do you need to find?

How many balloons of each color did Jada buy?

Answer 4 and 5 to **plan and solve** the problem.

You can solve the problem by acting out the problem with color tiles.

4. Count out 16 tiles. Separate 7 of them for the yellow balloons. How many red and blue balloons did Jada buy? __9__

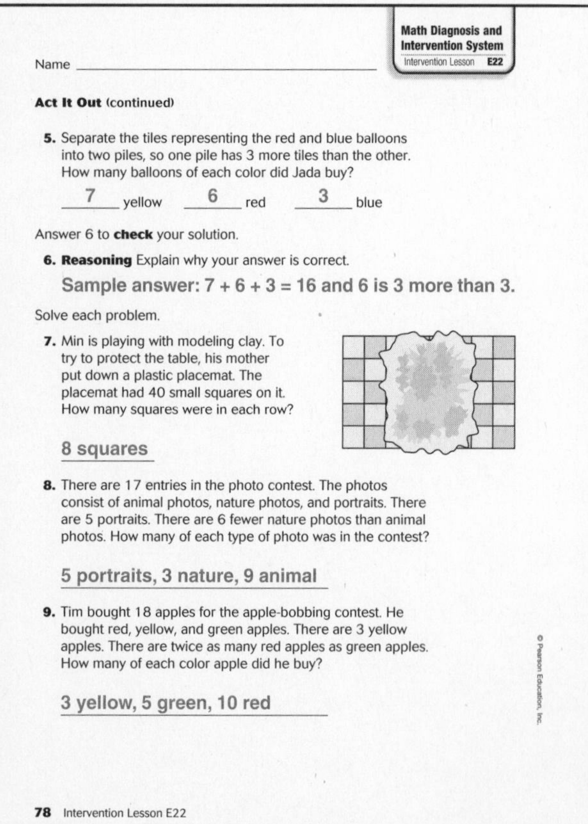
Math Diagnosis and Intervention System
Intervention Lesson E22

Name ______________________

Act It Out (continued)

5. Separate the tiles representing the red and blue balloons into two piles, so one pile has 3 more tiles than the other. How many balloons of each color did Jada buy?

__7__ yellow __6__ red __3__ blue

Answer 6 to **check** your solution.

6. Reasoning Explain why your answer is correct.

Sample answer: 7 + 6 + 3 = 16 and 6 is 3 more than 3.

Solve each problem.

7. Min is playing with modeling clay. To try to protect the table, his mother put down a plastic placemat. The placemat had 40 small squares on it. How many squares were in each row?

8 squares

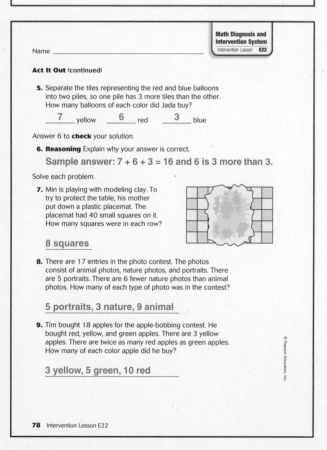

8. There are 17 entries in the photo contest. The photos consist of animal photos, nature photos, and portraits. There are 5 portraits. There are 6 fewer nature photos than animal photos. How many of each type of photo was in the contest?

5 portraits, 3 nature, 9 animal

9. Tim bought 18 apples for the apple-bobbing contest. He bought red, yellow, and green apples. There are 3 yellow apples. There are twice as many red apples as green apples. How many of each color apple did he buy?

3 yellow, 5 green, 10 red

Teacher Notes

Ongoing Assessment

Observe students use the color tiles in the exercises. Ask students who do not use the tiles how they solved the problem.

Error Intervention

If students have trouble solving the problem about Min's placemat,

then have students combine their color tiles to model the placemat

If You Have More Time

Have 16 students come to the front of the room to present Jada's balloons. Have students who are still sitting direct them where to move to act out the problem.

Make an Organized List

Math Diagnosis and Intervention System
Intervention Lesson E23

Name

Make an Organized List

Materials 4 index cards cut in half to make 8 halves

Veronica is playing a game called *Guess the Number*. What are all the possible numbers that fit the clues shown on the right? How many numbers are there?

Clues
It is a 3-digit odd number.
The hundreds digit is less than 3.
The tens digit is greater than 6.
The ones digit is greater than 6.

Solve by answering 1 to 10.

Answer 1 to 5 to **understand** the problem.

1. What do you know from reading the problem?

The number has 3 digits and is odd.

The hundreds digit is less than 3.

Both the tens and ones digits are greater than 6.

2. What do you need to find?

What are all the possible numbers that fit the clues? How many numbers are there?

3. What digits can be in the hundreds place? 1 or 2

4. What digits can be in the tens place? 7, 8, 9

5. What digits can be in the ones place? 7 or 9

Answer 6 to 9 to **plan and solve** the problem.

6. Write the possible digits for each place on index cards.

Math Diagnosis and Intervention System
Intervention Lesson E23

Name

Make an Organized List (continued)

You can solve the problem by making an organized list.

7. Put the cards with the smallest digits for each place together. What is one possible number?

177

This number is first in the list at the right.

8. Change the card for the ones digit and write another number in the list at the right. When you use all the ones cards, change the tens digit card to the next highest digit and match it with each possible ones digit. Continue in this organized way until you have listed all the possible numbers.

9. How many numbers are possible? 12

Hundreds	Tens	Ones
1	7	7
1	7	9
1	8	7
1	8	9
1	9	7
1	9	9
2	7	7
2	7	9
2	8	7
2	8	9
2	9	7
2	9	9

Answer 10 to **look back** at how you solved the problem.

10. Did you answer the right question? yes

Complete each list to solve.

11. The cups used to sell drinks at the game come in packages of 100 or 10. How many different ways can 320 cups be bought?

4 ways

Packages of 100	Packages of 10
3	2
2	12
1	22
0	32

12. You have black pants and tan pants. You have 3 shirts: black, red, and green. How many different outfits can you make?

6 different outfits

B–B T—B
B–R T—R
B–G T—G

Teacher Notes

Ongoing Assessment

Ask: ***Why does it help to organize your list when you are trying to find all possible answers?*** It's easier to make sure you have all possible answers when the list is organized than when it isn't organized.

Error Intervention

If students have trouble with place-value concepts,

then let them use place-value blocks and use A89 or F1: Ways to Show Numbers.

If You Have More Time

Have 3 students come to the front of the room and stand side-by-side. As the students change positions in an organized way, have the rest of the class make a list of the orders using the first initial of each student's name. There are 6 arrangements.

Try, Check, and Revise

Math Diagnosis and Intervention System
Intervention Lesson E24

Name ______________________

Try, Check, and Revise

The Koch family bought 5 tickets at the prices shown on the sign at the right. They spent $36. How many tickets of each type did they buy?

TICKETS	
Adults	$9 each
Children	$6 each

Solve by answering 1 to 8.

Answer 1 to 3 to **understand** the problem.

1. What do you know from reading the problem?
The Koch family bought 5 tickets and spent 36.

2. What do you know from reading the sign?
Adult's tickets cost $9 and children's tickets cost $6.

3. What do you need to find?
How many tickets of each type did the Koch family buy?

Answer 4 to 7 to **plan and solve** the problem.

You can solve the problem by using the strategy Try, Check, and Revise.

4. Suppose you guess that the Koch family bought 3 adult and 2 children's tickets. Check your guess. How much do 3 adult's and 2 children's tickets cost? $39

5. Is the cost too high, too low, or just right? too high

6. How can you change your guess to get a lower total?
Increase the number of children's tickets and decrease the adult ones.

7. Revise the guess and try again until the total cost is $36. How many tickets of each type did the Koch family buy?
They bought 2 adult's and 3 children's tickets.

Math Diagnosis and Intervention System
Intervention Lesson E24

Name ______________________

Try, Check, and Revise (continued)

Answer 8 to **look back** at how you solved the problem.

8. Explain how to use Try, Check, and Revise to solve a problem.
First you guess an answer to try. Then you check to see if the answer is the solution. If it isn't, you revise your guess to make it better. Then you check the new solution. You repeat this process until you get the right answer.

For Exercises 9 to 11, use the table at the right.

Camping Town	
Sleeping bag	$10
Flashlight	$3
Lantern	$5
Canteen	$4
Dried food	$2

9. Karen bought 2 different items. She spent $8. Which items did she buy?
Karen bought a flashlight and lantern.

10. Jake bought 3 different items. He spent a total of $15. Which items did he buy?
Jake bought a sleeping bag, flashlight, and dried food.

11. Adam spent $19 at Camping Town on 4 items. Two of his items were the same. What did he buy?
Adam bought a sleeping bag, lantern, and 2 dried foods.

Solve each problem.

12. Gina has twice as many goldfish as zebra fish. Together, there are 42 of these two types of fish in her tank. How many goldfish and zebra fish does she have?
Gina has 14 zebra fish and 28 goldfish in her tank.

13. Josh delivers pizza. In his money pouch are 6 bills worth $18. If he only has $1 and $5 bills, how many of each bill does he have?
Josh has three $5 bills and three $1 bills.

Teacher Notes

Ongoing Assessment

Ask: ***Adult's tickets cost $9 each and children's tickets cost $6 each. A family spent $24. You guess they bought 1 adult and 2 children's tickets, which comes to $21. What would be a good second guess?*** 2 adult's and 1 children's ticket, ***Why?*** $21 is too low, so change a lower priced ticket to a higher price, to increase the overall cost.

Error Intervention

If students do not know how to multiply to find, for example, the cost of 3 adult's tickets,

then encourage them to use addition.

If You Have More Time

Chose one student as a ticket seller and put prices for two types of tickets on the board or overhead. Have another students go up to the ticket seller and say, for instance, "I need 4 tickets that cost a total of $30." The ticket seller must decide how many of each type of ticket the buyer needs. Then, let the buyer become the ticket seller until all students have had a turn buying and selling. The first seller is the last buyer.

Draw a Picture and Write a Number Sentence

Math Diagnosis and Intervention System
Intervention Lesson E25

Name ______________________

Draw a Picture and Write a Number Sentence

The Bulldogs basketball team scored 38 points in the first half of the game. In the second half of the game the team scored 46 points. How many points did the Bulldogs score in the entire game?

Solve by answering 1 to 7.

Answer 1 and 2 to **understand** the problem.

1. What do you know from reading the problem?

The Bulldogs scored __38__ points in the first half of the game.

The Bulldogs scored __46__ points in the second half of the game.

2. What do you need to find?

How many points did the Bulldogs score in the entire game?

Answer 3 to 6 to **plan and solve** the problem.

You can solve the problem by drawing a picture and writing a number sentence.

3. Complete the picture at the right to show what you know.

?	
38	46

4. You know both parts and need to find the total. Do you add or subtract?

__add__

5. Write a number sentence to solve. __38 + 46 = 84__

6. How many points did the Bulldogs score in the entire game? __84__ points

Intervention Lesson E25 **83**

Math Diagnosis and Intervention System
Intervention Lesson E25

Name ______________________

Draw a Picture and Write a Number Sentence (continued)

Answer 7 to **look back** at how you solved the problem.

7. Reasoning Use estimation to explain why your answer is reasonable.

Sample answer: The Bulldogs scored about 40 points the first half and about 50 points the second half, which is about 90 points in all. Since 84 is close to 90, the answer of 84 is reasonable.

8. How many more points did the Bulldogs score in the second half than in the first half? Complete the picture at the right and write a number sentence to solve.

46	
38	?

Number sentence: __46 − 38 = 8__ __8__ more points

Draw a picture and write a number sentence to solve each problem.

9. There are 17 Asian elephants and 12 African elephants in the zoo. What is the total number of elephants in the zoo?

?	
17	12

Number sentence: __17 + 12 = 29__ __29__ elephants

10. Maggie wants to buy a set of paints for her art class. The cost of the paints is $49. She has saved $17 from her allowance so far. How much more money does she need to buy the set of paints?

49	
17	?

Number sentence: __49 − 17 = 32__ $__32__ more

11. The McKay family needs to drive 212 miles to reach the beach for a family vacation. If they have traveled 85 miles, how many more miles do they need to travel?

212	
85	?

Number sentence: __212 − 85 = 127__ __127__ more miles

84 Intervention Lesson E25

Teacher Notes

Ongoing Assessment

Ask: ***If you know the total and one part, do you need to add or subtract to find the other part?*** subtract

Error Intervention

If students have trouble with the computations,

then use some of the intervention lessons on adding and subtracting whole numbers C28, C29, C33, and C34 or G9, G10, G12, and G13.

If You Have More Time

Give students the distances between a large city you live in or near (City B) and each of two other cities (City A and City C). Have them draw a picture and write a number sentence to find how far it is from City A to City B and then to City C. Then have them do the same to find how much farther it is from City B to City A than from City B to City C.

Draw a Picture and Write a Number Sentence

Math Diagnosis and Intervention System
Intervention Lesson **E26**

Name ______________________

Math Diagnosis and Intervention System
Intervention Lesson E26

Draw a Picture and Write a Number Sentence

For the science project, Ms. Trapp needs 27 paper towel rolls for each of her 3 classes. How many rolls does she need in all?

Solve by answering 1 to 7.

Answer 1 and 2 to **understand** the problem.

1. What do you know from reading the problem?

Ms. Trapp needs __27__ paper towel rolls for each class.

Ms. Trapp has __3__ classes.

2. What do you need to find?

How many paper towel rolls does Ms. Trapp need in all?

Answer 3 to 5 to **plan and solve** the problem.

You can solve the problem by drawing a picture and writing a number sentence.

3. Complete the picture at the right to show what you know.

? paper towel rolls

27	27	27

Paper towel rolls needed for each

4. Write a number sentence to solve.

$3 \times 27 = 81$

5. How many paper towel rolls does Ms. Trapp need in all? __81__ paper towel rolls

Answer 6 and 7 to **look back and check** how you solved the problem.

6. Did you answer the right question? __yes__

Name ______________________

Math Diagnosis and Intervention System
Intervention Lesson E26

Draw a Picture and Write a Number Sentence (continued)

7. Reasoning Use estimation to explain why your answer is reasonable.

Sample answer: Ms. Trapp needs about 30 paper towel rolls for each class and $3 \times 30 = 90$. Since 81 is close to 90, the answer of 81 is reasonable.

Draw a picture and write a number sentence to solve each problem.

8. The catering company ordered 16 tablecloths. They also ordered 8 times as many napkins. How many napkins did they order?

tablecloths | 16 |

napkins	16	16	16	16	16	16	16	16	8 times as many

? napkins in all

Number sentence: $8 \times 16 = 128$ __128__ napkins

9. Mr. and Mrs. Gordon have 11 grandsons and 8 granddaughters. How many grandchildren do the Gordons have?

?

11	8

Number sentence: $11 + 8 = 19$ __19__ grandchildren

10. Yul bought a case for his CDs. Each page in the case holds 4 CDs. The case has 24 pages. How many CDs can the case hold?

__?__ CDs in all

24	24	24	24

CDs on each page

Number sentence: $4 \times 24 = 96$ __96__ CDs

11. Amy and Todd have blown up 34 balloons for a birthday party. Amy has blown up 18 balloons. How many did Todd blow up?

34

18	?

Number sentence: $34 - 18 = 16$ __16__ balloons

Teacher Notes

Ongoing Assessment

Ask: ***If Ms. Trapp needed 27 paper towel rolls for one class, 28 for another, and 25 for the third, could you multiply?*** no ***Why not?*** All groups must be the same size to multiply.

Error Intervention

If students do not understand concepts of multiplication,

then use some of the intervention lessons on multiplication concepts, B43 to B46 or G21 to G24.

If students have trouble with the computations,

then use C47 or G49: Multiplying Two-Digit Numbers.

If You Have More Time

Tell students how many students are in the class and how many classes are in the school. Have them write a number sentence and solve it to find how many students would be in the school if all the classes were the same size as theirs.

Draw a Picture and Write a Number Sentence

Math Diagnosis and Intervention System
Intervention Lesson E27

Name ______________________

Draw a Picture and Write a Number Sentence

The pet store ordered 24 hamsters. They put the hamsters in 6 different cages. If each cage had the same number of hamsters, how many hamsters were put in each cage?

Solve by answering 1 to 6.

Answer 1 and 2 to **understand** the problem.

1. What do you know from reading the problem?

The pet store ordered __24__ hamsters.

The pet store put the hamsters in __6__ different cages, with the same number of hamsters in each cage.

2. What do you need to find?

How many hamsters were put in each cage?

Answer 3 to 5 to **plan and solve** the problem.

You can solve the problem by drawing a picture and writing a number sentence.

3. Complete the picture at the right to show what you know.

__24__ hamsters

?	?	?	?	?	?

Hamsters in each cage

4. Write a number sentence to solve.

$24 \div 6 = 4$

5. How many hamsters were put in each cage? __4__ hamsters

Answer 6 to **look back** at how you solved the problem.

6. Did you answer the right question? __yes__

Math Diagnosis and Intervention System
Intervention Lesson E27

Name ______________________

Draw a Picture and Write a Number Sentence (continued)

Draw a picture and write a number sentence to solve each problem.

7. The florist ordered 36 vases. The vases were packaged 4 to a box. How many boxes were delivered to the florist?

__36__ vases

4 ....→ __?__ boxes

Vases in each box

Number sentence: $36 \div 4 = 9$

__9__ boxes

8. Johnston has 6 rolls of quarters. Each roll has 40 quarters. How many quarters does Johnston have?

__?__ quarters in all

40	40	40	40	40	40

Quarters in each roll

Number sentence: $6 \times 40 = 240$

__240__ quarters

9. Coach Yellowstone ordered 40 basketballs. He put them in 5 different bins. If each bin had the same number of basketballs, how many basketballs were put in each bin?

__40__ basketballs

?	?	?	?	?

Basketballs in each bin

Number sentence: $40 \div 5 = 8$

__8__ basketballs

10. Emily scored 7 times as many points on the video game as Roberta. Roberta scored 86 points. How many points did Emily score?

Roberta | 86 |

Emily | 86 | 86 | 86 | 86 | 86 | 86 | 86 | 7 times as many

__?__ points

Number sentence: $7 \times 86 = 602$

__602__ points

Teacher Notes

Ongoing Assessment

Ask: ***If you know the total and the number of groups, do you multiply or divide to find how many are in each group?*** divide

Error Intervention

If students do not understand concepts of division,

then use B57 or G35: Meanings for Division.

If You Have More Time

Have students write their own problem and draw a picture to illustrate it. Have them explain how to draw a picture and write a number sentence to solve the problem on the back of the page. Collect all the problems. If you started a problem solving book in intervention lesson J1 or J2, add these problems to it. Otherwise, bind the problems in a book titled "Our Problem Solving Book." When you have a few extra minutes, use the problems as a filler.

Solve a Simpler Problem

Math Diagnosis and Intervention System
Intervention Lesson **E28**

Name ______________________

Math Diagnosis and Intervention System
Intervention Lesson E28

Solve a Simpler Problem

A diagram of a flower garden in the city park is shown on the right. The garden is made of rose bushes and marigolds. The shaded part of the figure shows the part of the garden that is marigolds. What is the area of the shaded part of the flower garden?

□ = 1 square yard

Solve by answering 1 to 6.

Answer 1 and 2 to **understand** the problem.

1. What do you know from reading the problem?

The diagram shows a garden. The shaded part shows the part with marigolds.

The rest of the garden has roses.

2. What do you need to find?

What is the area of the shaded part of the flower garden?

Answer 3 to 5 to **plan and solve** the problem.

You can solve the problem by solving two simpler problems first.

3. What is the area of the whole garden?

$8 \times 6 = 48$

4. What is the area of the part that is not shaded?

$4 \times 2 = 8$

5. The area of the shaded part is the whole area minus the part that is not shaded. What is the area of the shaded part?

$48 - 8 = 40$ square yards

Name ______________________

Math Diagnosis and Intervention System
Intervention Lesson E28

Solve a Simpler Problem (continued)

Answer 6 to **look back** at how you solved the problem.

6. Explain how to use Solving a Simpler Problem to solve a problem.

Sample answer: First you solve part of the problem, that is easier to solve than the whole problem. Then you use the answers you get to solve the original problem.

Solve each problem.

Use the grid at the right for Exercises 7 and 8. Be careful, arrows show one-way streets.

North
West
East
Grandma's
Store
Home
= 1 block
South

7. Find the distance (the number of blocks) from home to the store and then to Grandma's.

8 blocks

8. Sara started from home, drove 5 blocks north, 3 blocks west, and 4 blocks south, but she still needed to go to the store. How many blocks was she from the store?

1 block

Gloria tiled her bathroom floor. She used white and gray tiles as shown at the right. Use the diagram for Exercises 9 and 10.

□ = 1 square foot

9. What is the gray area?

48 ft^2

10. How much greater is the gray area than the white area?

36 ft^2

Teacher Notes

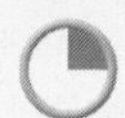

Ongoing Assessment

Ask: ***What is another way to find the area of the shaded part of the flower garden by solving simpler problems?*** Divide it into 4 rectangles and add the areas. One way to do this is to use two rectangles that are 2 by 6 that have an area of twelve plus two rectangles that are 4 by 2 that have an area of 8. So, the total area is $12 + 12 + 8 + 8 = 40$ square yards.

Error Intervention

If students have trouble with area or coordinate grid concepts,

then use D45 or I44: Finding Area on a Grid and D81 or F30: Graphing Oredered Pairs.

If You Have More Time

Have students color a rectangle on grid paper, leaving a rectangle or square uncolored inside. Then have them find the area they colored.

Make a Graph

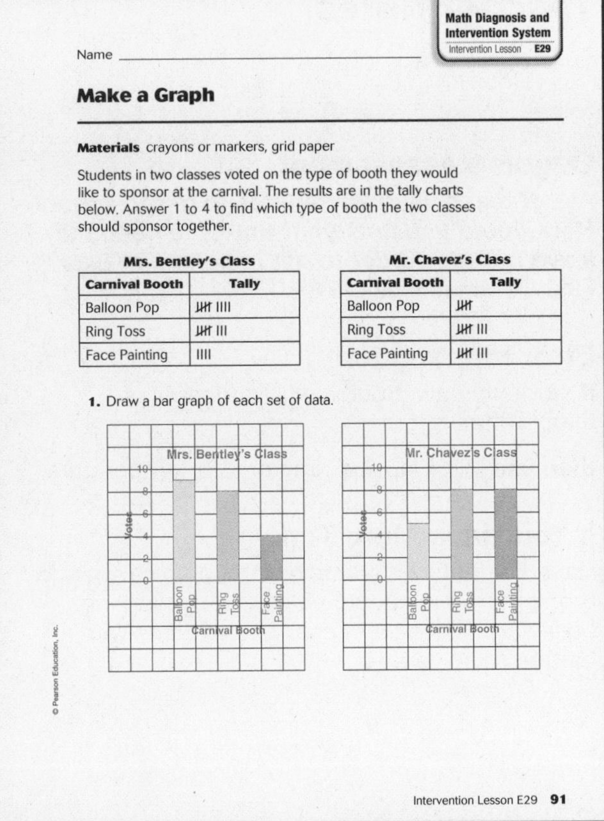
Math Diagnosis and Intervention System
Intervention Lesson E29

Name ______________________

Make a Graph

Materials crayons or markers, grid paper

Students in two classes voted on the type of booth they would like to sponsor at the carnival. The results are in the tally charts below. Answer 1 to 4 to find which type of booth the two classes should sponsor together.

Mrs. Bentley's Class

Carnival Booth	Tally
Balloon Pop	𝍸 IIII
Ring Toss	𝍸 III
Face Painting	IIII

Mr. Chavez's Class

Carnival Booth	Tally
Balloon Pop	𝍸
Ring Toss	𝍸 III
Face Painting	𝍸 III

1. Draw a bar graph of each set of data.

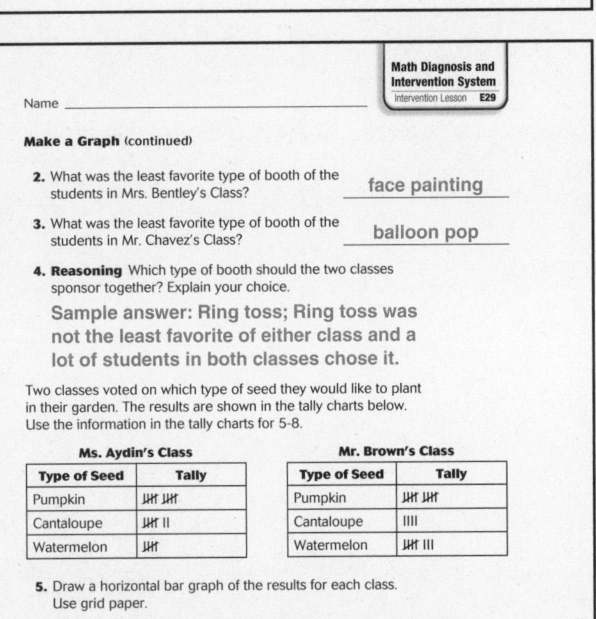
Math Diagnosis and Intervention System
Intervention Lesson E29

Name ______________________

Make a Graph (continued)

2. What was the least favorite type of booth of the students in Mrs. Bentley's Class? face painting
3. What was the least favorite type of booth of the students in Mr. Chavez's Class? balloon pop
4. **Reasoning** Which type of booth should the two classes sponsor together? Explain your choice.
   Sample answer: Ring toss; Ring toss was not the least favorite of either class and a lot of students in both classes chose it.

Two classes voted on which type of seed they would like to plant in their garden. The results are shown in the tally charts below. Use the information in the tally charts for 5-8.

Ms. Aydin's Class

Type of Seed	Tally
Pumpkin	𝍸 𝍸
Cantaloupe	𝍸 II
Watermelon	𝍸

Mr. Brown's Class

Type of Seed	Tally
Pumpkin	𝍸 𝍸
Cantaloupe	IIII
Watermelon	𝍸 III

5. Draw a horizontal bar graph of the results for each class. Use grid paper.
   Graphs are shown on the Teacher Notes page.
6. Which seed got the same number of votes from both classes? pumpkin
7. Cantaloupe got more votes from which class? Ms. Aydin's Class
8. **Reasoning** Was the favorite seed the same for both classes? Explain how you can tell from the graphs.
   Yes, pumpkin was the favorite of both classes. The bar for pumpkin was the longest on both graphs.

Teacher Notes

Ongoing Assessment

Observe to see which students use the graphs to compare the data between classes and which use the tally charts.

Error Intervention

If students have trouble drawing or reading the bar graph,

then use I61: Reading and Making a Bar Graph.

If You Have More Time

Have students write more comparisons they can make based on the graphs they drew.

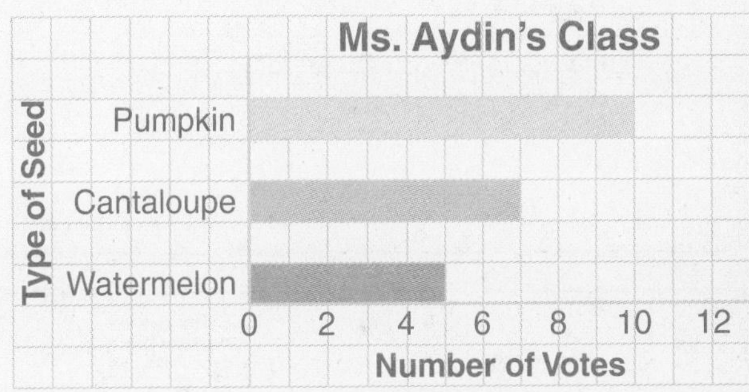

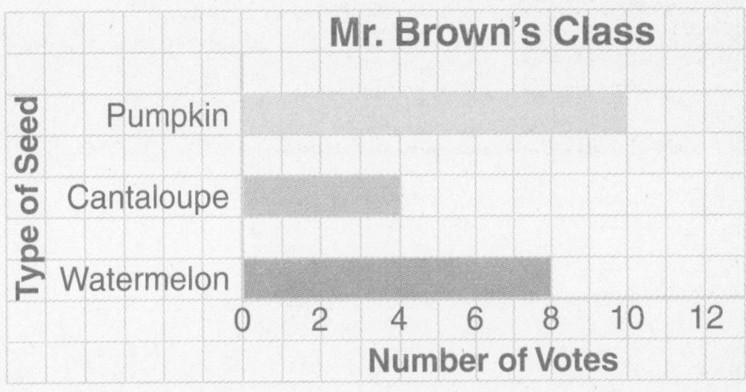

Work Backward

Math Diagnosis and Intervention System
Intervention Lesson E30

Name ______________________

Work Backward

Between 4:00 P.M. and 5:00 P.M., the temperature dropped 4 degrees. Every hour after that, the temperature dropped 2 degrees. At 8:00 P.M., the temperature was 52°F. What was the temperature at 4:00 P.M.?

F 70 60 50 40
8:00 P.M.

Solve by answering 1 to 7.

Answer 1 and 2 to **understand** the problem.

1. What do you know from reading the problem?

The temperature dropped __4__ degrees, between 4:00 P.M. and 5:00 P.M.

The temperature dropped __2__ degrees, every hour after 5:00 P.M.

The temperature was __52°F__, at 8:00 P.M.

2. What do you need to find?

What was the temperature at 4:00 P.M.?

Answer 3 to 5 to **plan and solve** the problem.

You can solve by working backward.

3. The temperature dropped 2 degrees from 7:00 P.M. to 8:00 P.M. The temperature was 52°F at 8:00 P.M. What was the temperature at 7:00 P.M.? Write your answer in the diagram below.

4:00 P.M.	5:00 P.M.	6:00 P.M.	7:00 P.M.	8:00 P.M.
−4 →	−2 →	−2 →	−2 →	
62°F	58°F	56°F	54°F	52°F
← +4	← +2	← +2	← +2	

Math Diagnosis and Intervention System
Intervention Lesson E30

Name ______________________

Work Backward (continued)

4. Find the temperature at 6:00 P.M., then 5:00 P.M., then 4:00 P.M. Write each in the diagram on the previous page.

5. What was the temperature at 4:00 P.M.? __62°F__

Answer 6 and 7 to **look back and check** your solution to the problem.

6. The temperature dropped 2 degrees from 7:00 P.M. to 8:00 P.M., which means you subtract 2. When working backward from 8:00 P.M. to 7:00 P.M., do you add or subtract 2? __add__

7. If the temperature was the one you found at 4:00 P.M. and changed as described in the problem, would it be 52°F at 8:00 P.M.? __yes__

Solve each problem.

8. It takes Josh 10 minutes to get ready for soccer practice and 25 minutes to bike to the field. He needs to eat a snack before he gets ready and that takes 15 minutes. Soccer practice is at 4:30. What time does Josh need to start eating his snack to get to soccer practice on time? __3:40__

9. Lola took 45 minutes to get ready for school. She walked to school in 20 minutes and then waited 5 minutes before the bell rang at 8:55 A.M. What time did she get out of bed that morning?

__7:45 A.M.__

10. The trip from your home to the museum takes 45 minutes. You need 1 hour and 30 minutes to tour a special exhibit in the museum. You want to finish the tour before 3:00 P.M. What is the latest time you should leave home to go to the museum?

__12:45 P.M.__

Teacher Notes

Ongoing Assessment

Ask: ***It takes Jean 20 minutes to get to school. How would you find what time she needs to leave home in order to get to school at 8:30?*** Find 20 minutes before 8:30.

Error Intervention

If students have trouble with concepts of temperature or time,

then use I31: Elapsed Time or I32: Temperature.

If You Have More Time

Have students write time or temperature change problems, which could be solved by working backward. Have them change problems with a partner to solve.

Make and Test Generalizations

Math Diagnosis and Intervention System
Intervention Lesson E31

Name ____________________

Make and Test Generalizations

How are the polygons alike?

Polygon 1 Polygon 2 Polygon 3

Solve by answering 1 to 5.

1. Complete the generalization about the polygons.

   All the polygons have __6__ sides.

2. Test the generalization.

   Does Polygon 1 have 6 sides? __yes__ Polygon 2? __yes__

   Polygon 3? __yes__

   Since the generalization holds for all 3 polygons, it is true.

3. Test the following generalization: All the sides of each polygon are the same length.

   Are all the sides of Polygon 1 the same length? __yes__

   Are all the sides of Polygon 2 the same length? __no__

   Are all the sides of Polygon 3 the same length? __yes__

4. Is the conjecture true? __no__

5. **Reasoning** Is the following generalization true? All the polygons have at least one obtuse angle. Explain.

   Yes; Sample answer: Polygon 1 has obtuse angles, Polygon 2 has obtuse angles, and Polygon 3 has obtuse angles. The conjecture holds for all 3 polygons, so it is true.

Math Diagnosis and Intervention System
Intervention Lesson E31

Name ____________________

Make and Test Generalizations (continued)

Make a generalization about each set of figures. Test your generalization. If the generalization is not true, make another generalization until you find one that is true.

6. Sample answer: They all have intersecting lines.

7. N F A Z Y

   Sample answer: They are all made from 3 line segments.

8. Sample answer: They all have 1 right angle.

9. Sample answer: They are all rectangles.

10. Sample answer: They all include a curved side.

Teacher Notes

Ongoing Assessment

Ask: ***How can you make a generalization?*** Make a statement about a group of things that you think is true.

Error Intervention

If students have trouble with the geometry concepts,

then use D62 or I4: Acute, Right, and Obtuse Angles and D63 or I5: Polygons.

If You Have More Time

Have students work in pairs. Have one student draw a group of shapes that are alike in some way. Have the other student guess how the shapes are alike. Then, have them change roles and repeat.

Reasonableness

Math Diagnosis and Intervention System
Intervention Lesson E32

Name ______________________

Reasonableness

A container when empty weighs 150 pounds. If the container is filled with 312 pounds, what is the total weight of the container and its contents?

Solve by answering 1 to 7.

Answer 1 and 2 to **understand** the problem.

1. What do you know from reading the problem?

   The empty container weighs 150 pounds.

   The contents of the container weighs 312 pounds.

2. What do you need to find?

   What is the total weight of the container and its contents?

Answer 3 and 4 to **plan and solve** the problem.

3. How can you solve the problem? Add 150 and 312.
4. What is the total weight of the container and its contents? 462 pounds

Answer 5 to 7 to **check** that your answer is reasonable.

5. Estimate 150 + 312 by rounding to the nearest hundred.

   150 + 312 is about 500

6. Is your answer to the problem close to the estimate? yes

Since the answer of 462 is close to the estimate of 500, the answer 462 pounds is **reasonable**.

7. Did you answer the right question? yes

Math Diagnosis and Intervention System
Intervention Lesson E32

Name ______________________

Reasonableness (continued)

Solve each problem. Then explain why your answer is reasonable.

8. Karen had some stickers. She gave 34 butterfly stickers and 27 flag stickers to Bill. How many stickers did Karen give to Bill?

   Karen gave Bill 51 stickers. 34 + 27 is about 30 + 20 = 50. Since 51 is close to 50, the answer of 51 is reasonable.

9. Harold collects stamps. He has 32 stamps from the United States and 18 stamps from other countries. How many more United States stamps does Harold have than international stamps?

   Harold has 14 more United States stamps than international stamps. 32 − 18 is about 30 − 20 = 10. Since 14 is close to 10, the answer of 14 is reasonable.

10. Some students took a survey about cats and dogs. They found that 87 students like dogs and 56 students like cats. How many students voted for cats or dogs?

    143 students; 87 + 56 is about 90 + 60 = 150. Since 143 is close to 150, the answer of 143 is reasonable.

11. On Friday, 214 people came to the concert. On Saturday, 298 people came. How many people came on both nights combined?

    512 people; 214 + 298 is about 200 + 300 = 500. Since 512 is close to 512, the answer of 512 is reasonable.

12. At TV City, a new television costs $629. At Discount Place, the same TV costs $498. How much more does the TV cost at TV City than at Discount Place?

    $131; 629 − 498 is about 600 − 500 = 100. Since 131 is close to 100, the answer of 131 is reasonable.

Teacher Notes

Ongoing Assessment

Ask: ***Why is it a good idea to check that your answer is reasonable?*** You can avoid mistakes.

Error Intervention

If students have trouble with the computations,

then use C28 or G9: Adding Two-Digit Numbers, C29 or G10: Subtracting Two-Digit Numbers, C33 or G12: Adding Three-Digit Numbers, and C34 or G13: Subtracting Three-Digit Numbers.

If You Have More Time

Have students make up story problems and give an answer. Then have a partner tell whether or not the answer is reasonable. Have students change roles and repeat.

Write to Explain

Math Diagnosis and Intervention System
Intervention Lesson E33

Name ______________________

Write to Explain

Mr. Kerr wants to buy circus tickets for his family. Tickets cost $7 each. How much will it cost to buy 6 tickets?

Solve by answering 1 to 5.

Answer 1 and 2 to **understand** the problem.

1. What do you know from reading the problem?

Circus tickets cost __$7__ each.

2. What do you need to find?

How much does it cost to buy 6 circus tickets?

Answer 3 and 4 to **plan and solve** the problem.

You can solve the problem by making a table.

3. Complete the table.

Number of tickets	1	2	3	4	5	6
Cost	$7	$14	$21	$28	$35	$42

4. How much does it cost to buy 6 circus tickets? __$42__

Answer 5 to **look back** at the solution to the problem.

5. Fill in the blanks to complete the explanation of how to solve the problem.

One ticket cost $7, so two tickets cost $7 more. $7 + __$7__ = __$14__

Three ticket cost $7 more than 2 tickets. $14 + __$7__ = __$21__

Keep adding __$7__ to complete the table.

Six tickets cost __$42__.

Math Diagnosis and Intervention System
Intervention Lesson E33

Name ______________________

Write to Explain (continued)

6. Fill in the blanks to complete the explanation of how to solve the problem.

Mollie is taller than Kristin and shorter than Mike. Ted is shorter than Mollie but taller than Kristin. Who is the tallest?

Mollie is taller than __Kristin__

and shorter than __Mike__.

Draw a picture to show this information.

Kristin Mollie Mike

Ted is shorter than __Mollie__

but taller than __Kristin__.

Show this information in the picture.

The picture shows that the tallest is __Mike__.

Kristin Ted Mollie Mike

Write to explain.

7. Explain how the number of eggs changes as the number of dozens changes.

Dozens	1	2	3	4	5
Eggs	12	24	36	48	60

Sample answer: As the number of dozens increase by 1, the number of eggs increase by 12.

8. Four people can sit at each square table. Three tables are pushed together to form a long rectangular table. How many people can sit at this long table?

X X X
X X
X X X

8 people can sit at the long table.

Teacher Notes

Ongoing Assessment

Ask: ***Explain how to find the cost of 3 tickets if each one costs $5.*** Sample answer: One ticket costs $5, so two tickets cost 5 + 5 = $10, and three tickets cost 10 + 5 = $15.

Error Intervention

If students have trouble with the patterns,

then use D76: Input/Output Tables and E21: Make a Table and Look for a Pattern.

If You Have More Time

Have students give an oral explanation of how to solve a specific problem.

Name ______________________________

Extra Information

1. Omar has 5 red toy cars.
~~He has 4 books.~~
He has 3 blue toy cars.
How many cars does Omar have?

5 + 3 = 8 cars

2. 16 ducks are swimming on the pond.
6 frogs are in the pond.
9 ducks fly away.
How many ducks are left on the pond?

_____ − _____ = _____

3. 6 turtles are sitting in the sun.
5 turtles are swimming in the pond.
There are 3 lily pads in the pond.
How many turtles are there in all?

_____ + _____ = _____ turtles

1. Read the problem to the children. Help them understand by asking: ***What do you know?*** Omar has 5 red toy cars, 4 books, and 3 blue toy cars. ***What do you need to find?*** Find how many cars Omar has.
2. Ask: ***Do you need all the information given in the problem to solve?*** no ***What information is extra, not needed?*** Omar has 4 books is extra information. Have children cross out the sentence about 4 books.
3. Help children plan and solve by asking: ***How can you solve the problem?*** Add 5 and 3; Have children write a number sentence and solve.
4. Help children look back and check by asking: ***Did you answer the right question?*** Yes; 8 is the number of cars Omar has.
5. Do the other problems similarly.

Name ______________________________

Extra Information (continued)

Cross out the extra information.
Solve the problem.

4. ~~The library is 3 blocks from June's house.~~
June got 9 books on Monday.
She took back 4 books on Saturday.

How many books did she have left?

9 – 4 = 5 books

5. Buddy has 11 markers on his desk.
His friend gives him 3 more markers.
He has 6 pencils inside his desk.

How many markers does he have in all?

____ + ____ = ____ markers

6. Sandi found 12 shells at the beach.
Ira found 2 pails in the sand.
Ari found 8 shells.

How many more shells did Sandi find than Ari?

____ – ____ = ____ shells

7. 15 books are on a shelf.
2 books are on a table.
5 pictures are on the wall.

How many books are there in all?

____ + ____ = ____ books

Name ______________________________

Two-Question Problems

1. Luisa has 6 colored beads. She gets 3 more. How many beads does she have in all?

6 + 3 = 9 beads

Luisa gives 2 beads to Maria. How many beads does Luisa have left?

9 − 2 = 7 beads left

2. Kevin has 4 books. He gets 4 more books. How many books does he have in all?

_____ ○ _____ = _____ books

Kevin gives away 3 of his books. How many books does he have now?

_____ ○ _____ = _____ books

1. Read the first part of the problem. Help children understand by asking: ***What do you know?*** Luisa has 6 colored beads and she gets 3 more. ***What do you need to find?*** Find how many beads Luisa has in all.
2. Help children plan and solve by asking: ***How can you solve the problem?*** Add 6 and 3; Have children write a number sentence and solve.
3. Read the second part of the problem. Ask: ***What do you know?*** Luisa has 9 beads and she gives 2 beads to Maria. ***How did you know Luisa has 9 beads?*** by solving the first part of the problem ***What do you need to find?*** Find how many beads Luisa has left.
4. Ask: ***How can you solve the problem?*** Find 9 minus 2; Have children write a number sentence and solve.
5. Help children look back by asking: ***How many questions did the problem have?*** 2
6. Do the other problem similarly.

Name ______________________________

Two-Question Problems (continued)

Solve each problem.

3. There are 10 flowers in a vase. 6 are roses. The rest are lilies. How many are lilies?

10 ⊖ 6 = 4 lilies

Sally took out 2 lilies.
How many lilies are left now?

_____ ◯ _____ = _____ lilies

4. Alberto has 7 pencils in his box. He gets 4 more. How many does he have in all?

_____ ◯ _____ = _____ pencils

He gives 5 pencils to Wen. How many does Alberto have left?

_____ ◯ _____ = _____ pencils

5. Eva has 12 markers. She gives 5 to some friends. How many does she have left?

_____ ◯ _____ = _____ markers

Eva's teacher gives her 3 more markers.
How many markers does Eva have now?

_____ ◯ _____ = _____ markers

Name ______________________________

Multiple-Step Problems

1. Soccer practice is 45 minutes long. The team spends 10 minutes warming up and 15 minutes on drills. How much time is left for games?

Step 1   Step 2

10   45
+ 15   − ☐
☐   ☐

_______ minutes

2. Niki had 12 stuffed animals and 6 dolls. She gave away 7 of the toys. How many toys did she have left?

Step 1   Step 2

☐   ☐
+ ☐   − ☐
☐   ☐

_______ toys

1. Read the problem to the children. Help them understand by asking: ***What do you know?*** Soccer practice is 45 minutes long, which includes 10 minutes to warm up and 15 minutes on drills. ***What do you need to find?*** Find how much time is left for games.
2. Help children plan and solve by asking: ***How can you find how much time is left for games?*** Find 45 minus the time spent warming up and doing drills. ***The problem has a hidden question. What do you need to find before you can subtract to find the time left for games?*** How many minutes does the team spend warming up and doing drills? Have students write the hidden question.
3. Ask: ***How can you find how many minutes the team spends warming up and doing drills?*** Add 10 and 15; Have children find the sum under step 1. ***Now, what do you need to subtract?*** 45 − 25; Have children find the difference under step 2. Ask: ***How many minutes are left for games?*** Have children write 20.
4. Help children look back and check by asking: ***Since practice is 45 minutes, should the time for games be more than 45 minutes or less than 45 minutes?*** less than 45 minutes ***Is 20 minutes less than 45 minutes?*** yes ***How did you solve the problem?*** Find and answer the hidden question.
5. Do the other problem similarly.

Name ______________________________

Multiple-Step Problems (continued)

Write the hidden question. Then solve.

3. Paco had 28 balloons for his birthday party. He gave away 21 at the party. After the party, 2 more burst. How many balloons did Paco have left then?

Hidden Question:

Step 1   Step 2

□   □
− □   − □
□   □

_______ balloons

4. Becky practiced piano 34 minutes Saturday morning and 16 minutes Saturday afternoon. If she also practiced 22 minutes on Friday, how many minutes did she practice in all?

Hidden Question:

Step 1   Step 2

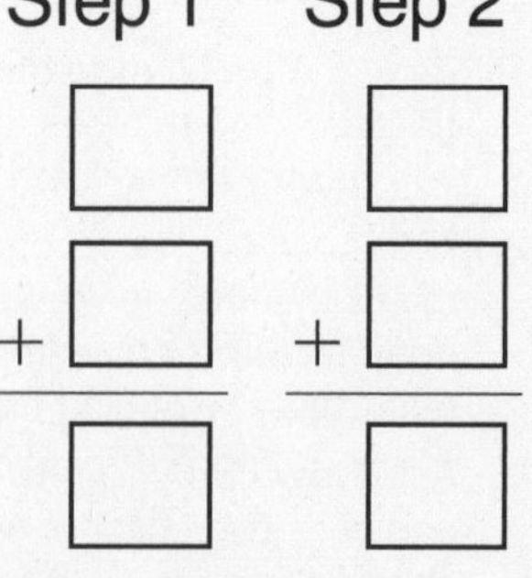

_______ minutes

Name ______________________________

Use Data from a Table or Chart

1. __________

2. ________________

3. 

____

4. _______ pounds

5. ________________

6. ________________

Silly Sports Day	
Time	**Activity**
9:30	Egg on a Spoon
10:00	Ball Bounce
10:30	Hopping Race
11:00	Book Balance
11:30	Lunch
12:30	Cartwheels
1:00	Tiptoe Race

Weights of 5 Dogs	
Buddy	70 pounds
Fido	43 pounds
Socks	35 pounds
Tip	60 pounds
Vinny	15 pounds

1. Introduce the schedule. Ask: ***What time does the Ball Bounce begin?*** Have children find Ball Bounce in the schedule table. Ask: ***What time is in the same row as Ball Bounce?*** 10:00 ***This means the Ball Bounce starts at 10:00.*** Have children write the time as the answer to item 1.
2. Ask: ***What begins at 11:00?*** Have children find 11:00 in the table. Ask: ***What activity is in the same row as 11:00?*** Have children write Book Balance as the answer to item 2.
3. Ask: ***What begins at the time shown on the clock? To solve, first you need to find the time on the clock. What time is shown on the clock?*** Have children find 12:30 in the table. Ask: ***What activity is in the same row as 12:30?*** Have children write Cartwheels as the answer to item 3.
4. Introduce the second table. Ask: ***How much does Buddy weigh?*** Have children write 70 as the answer to item 4.
5. Ask: ***Which dog weighs 60 pounds?*** Have children write Tip as the answer to item 5.
6. Ask: ***Which dog weighs more than 40 pounds but less than 50 pounds?*** Have children put an x next to each weight that is not more than 40 pounds. Then have them put an x next to each weight that is not less than 50 pounds. Ask what is left. Have children write Fido as the answer to item 6.

Name ______________________________

Use Data from a Table or Chart (continued)

Use the table to answer the questions.

Field Day

Time	Event
1:00 – 1:30	Parade
1:30 – 2:00	Relay Race
2:00 – 2:30	Cross-Country Race
2:30 – 3:00	100-Yard Dash

7. What time does the Relay Race begin? __________

8. What begins at 2:30? ______________________

9. What begins at the time shown on the clock?

____

10. Pick three events and make a schedule for yourself.

Time	Event
10:00-10:30	
10:30-11:15	
11:15-11:45	

Name ______________________________

Missing or Extra Information

Sally's painting is 14 inches long and 12 inches wide. Julie's painting is 16 inches long. How much longer is Julie's painting then Sally's painting?

Solve by answering 1 to 7.

Answer 1 to 4 to **understand** the problem.

1. What do you know from reading the problem?

Sally's painting is ______________ long.

Sally's painting is ______________ wide.

Julie's painting is ______________ long.

2. What do you need to find?

3. Do you have all the information you need to solve the problem? ______

4. What information is not needed to solve the problem?

Answer 5 and 6 to **plan and solve** the problem.

5. How can you solve the problem? ______________________________

6. Solve. How much longer is Julie's painting than Sally's painting? ______ inches

Answer 7 to **look back** at how you solved the problem.

7. Is your answer reasonable? ______

Name ______________________________

Missing or Extra Information (continued)

How much wider is Sally's painting than Julie's?

Find out by answering 8 and 9.

8. Do you have all the information you need to solve the problem? _______

9. What do you need to know in order to solve the problem?

So, there is not enough information to solve the problem.

Write the extra or missing information. Solve the problem if enough information is given.

10. Jason bought a red sweater and a black sweater. His change was $5. How much did Jason pay for both sweaters?

Write the extra or missing information. Solve the problem if enough information is given.

Use the graph for Exercises 11 and 12.

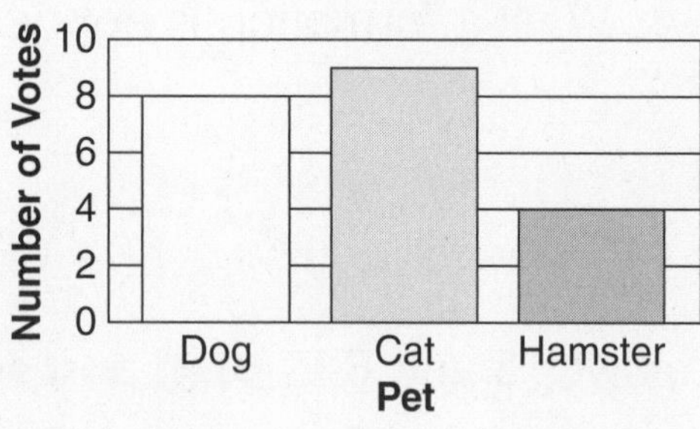

11. Turtles received 4 fewer votes than cats and 2 more votes than rabbits. How many votes did turtles receive?

12. How many more students voted for dogs than horses?

13. Reasoning Rose's painting is 12 inches long. Will it fit in a frame that has length of 12 inches and a width of 8 inches? Explain.

Name ______________________________

Two-Question Problems

Max earns $9 for every hour he rakes leaves. It took him 2 hours to rake the leaves in his yard. How much money did he earn raking leaves? If he already had $26, how much does he have now?

Solve by answering 1 to 7.

Answer 1 and 2 to **understand** the problem.

1. What do you know from reading the problem?

Max earns _______ for every hour he rakes leaves.

He raked leaves for _______ hours.

He already had _______.

2. What do you need to find?

The problem has two questions. Answer the first one. Then, answer the second one.

Answer 3 to 6 to **plan and solve** the problem.

3. How can you answer the first question? ______________________

4. Solve. How much did Max earn raking leaves? _______

5. How can you answer the second question? ______________________

6. Solve. How much money did Max have after raking leaves? _______

Name ____________________

Two-Question Problems (continued)

Answer 7 to **check** your solution.

7. **Reasoning** Use an estimate to explain why your answer to how much money Max has now is reasonable.

Solve each problem. Answer both questions.

8. Ms. Olivia brought 7 bunches of bananas to the school picnic. Each bunch had 5 bananas. She also brought 27 apples.

   How many bananas did she bring? _______ bananas

   How many more bananas than apples did Ms. Olivia bring? _______ more

9. There are 3 children and 2 adults in Zac's family. Each person in the family donated $5 to charity.

   How many people are in Zac's family? _______ people

   How much money did Zac's family donate to charity? _______

10. Monique read 45 pages on Saturday and 39 pages on Sunday. Her book has 113 pages.

    How many pages did Monique read? _______ pages

    How many more pages does she need to read to finish her book? _______ pages

11. Tandy bought 4 boxes of cat treats. Each box contains 2 packages. It takes 5 days to use each package of cat treats.

    How many packages of cat treats did Tandy buy? _______ packages

    How many days worth of cat treats did Tandy buy? _______ days

Name ____________________

Multiple-Step Problems

At the sports store, Hannah bought 2 baseballs, and Jim bought 3 baseballs. The baseballs cost $6 each. How much did they spend?

Solve by answering 1 to 8.

Answer 1 and 2 to **understand** the problem.

1. What do you know from reading the problem?

Hannah bought ____________.

Jim bought ____________.

The baseballs cost ______ each.

2. What do you need to find?

Answer 3 to 7 to **plan and solve** the problem.

3. How can you find how much Hannah and Jim spent?

4. Does the problem tell you how many baseballs Hannah and Jim bought altogether? ______

5. Do you have enough information to find out how many baseballs Hannah and Jim bought altogether? ______

"How many baseballs did Hannah and Jim buy altogether?" is the **hidden question** in the problem. You need to answer the hidden question before you can solve the problem.

6. How many baseballs did Hannah and Jim buy altogether? ______

Name ______________________________

Multiple-Step Problems (continued)

7. How much money did Hannah and Jim spend on the baseballs? ________

Answer 8 to **look back and check** your solution to the problem.

8. Did you answer the right question? ________

Write and answer the hidden question. Then solve the problem.

9. Henry had 571 baseball cards. He sold 395 of them. He then bought 275 new baseball cards. How many cards does he have now?

Use the graph to answer Exercises 10 and 11.

10. How many students voted for fruit or cheese?

11. How many more students voted for pretzels than voted for sandwiches?

Favorite Snack	
Fruit	☺ ☺ ☺
Sandwiches	☺ ☺
Cheese	☺
Pretzels	☺ ☺ ☺ ☺

Each ☺ = 3 votes.

12. It costs $3 to rent a DVD. Sue rented 4 DVDs and Fran rented 3 DVDs. How much did they pay in all?

13. Reasoning Describe another way to find how much Sue and Fran paid in all for the DVDs in Exercise 12.

Name ______________________________

Multiple-Step Problems

Melanie mixed 64 ounces of pineapple juice and 32 ounces of cherry juice to make a punch. She then poured all the punch into cups, with 8 ounces in each cup. How many cups of punch did Melanie pour?

Solve by answering 1 to 8.

Answer 1 and 2 to **understand** the problem.

1. What do you know from reading the problem?

Melanie used ______________ of pineapple juice.

Melanie used ______________ of cherry juice.

Melanie poured ______________ of punch into each cup.

2. What do you need to find?

Answer 3 to 7 to **plan and solve** the problem.

3. How can you find how many cups of punch Melanie poured?

4. Does the problem tell you how many ounces of punch Melanie made? ______

5. Do you have enough information to find out how many ounces of punch Melanie made? ______

"How many ounces of punch did Melanie make?" is the **hidden question** in the problem. You need to answer the hidden question before you can solve the problem.

Name ______________________________

Multiple-Step Problems (continued)

6. How many ounces of punch did Melanie make? _______ ounces

7. How many cups of punch did Melanie pour? _______ cups

Answer 8 to **look back** at your solution to the problem.

8. **Reasoning** Describe another way to find how many cups of punch Melanie poured.

Write and answer the hidden question. Then solve the problem.

9. Lacy bought 2 yards of blue material, 6 yards of red material, and 6 yards of white material, each for \$2 a yard. How much change did she receive if she paid with a \$50 bill?

10. Trevor spent \$34 on a video game at one store. Then at another store he spent a total of \$38 on two model cars. How much more did the video game cost than one model car if each model car cost the same?

11. Elise ordered 5 pounds of hamburger packaged in freezer paper and the rest packaged for immediate use. Her total bill was \$36. If each pound cost \$4, how many pounds of hamburger was packaged for immediate use?

Name ____________________________________

Look for a Pattern

1. 12 14 16 18

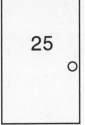

2. 15  20 25 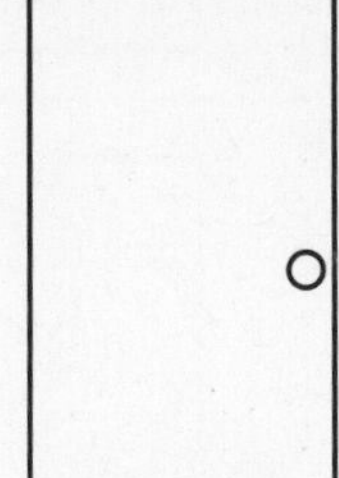 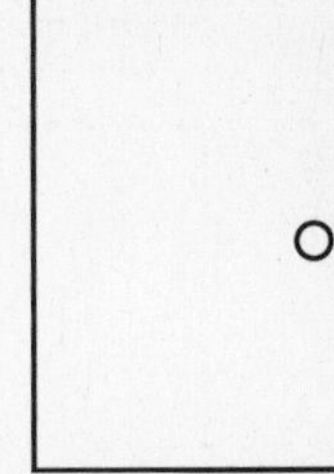

3. 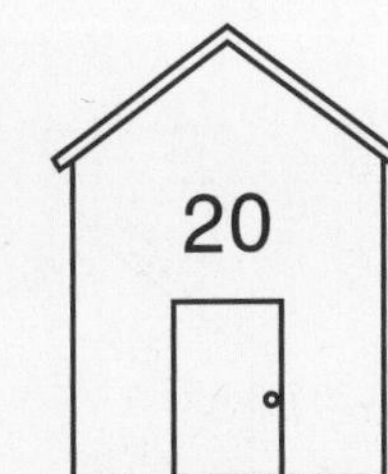

30
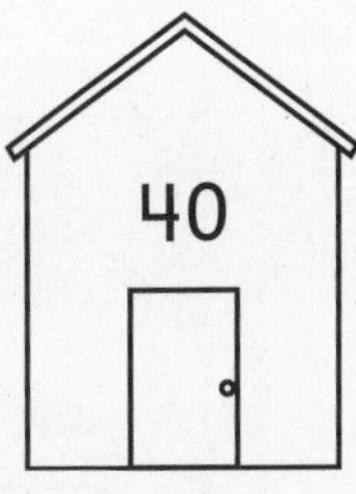

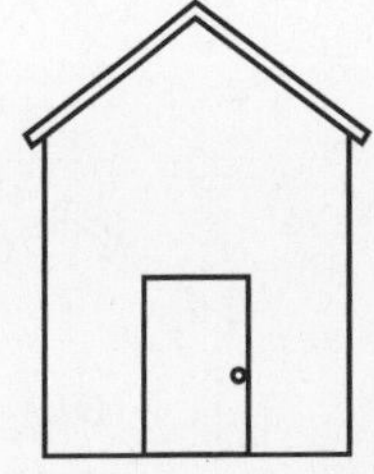 

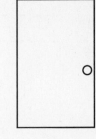

4. 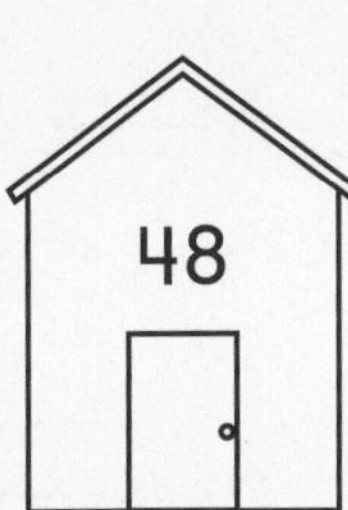

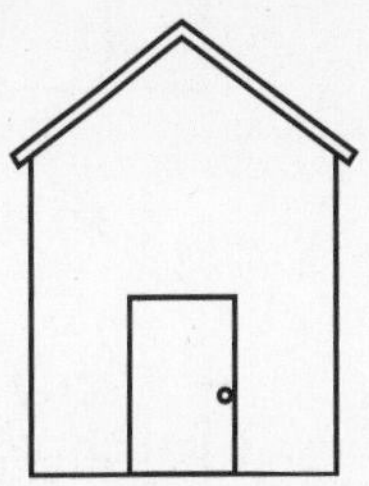 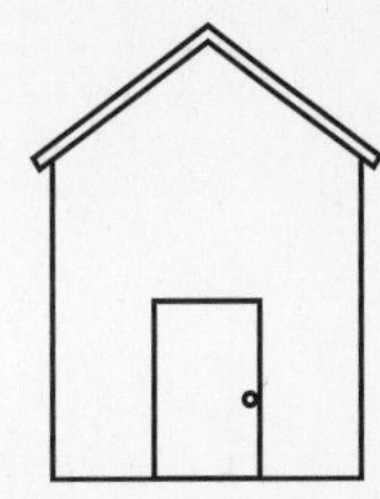

Materials: Snap cubes, 70 for each child or pair, 20 in one color and 10 in each of 5 other colors

1. Say: ***What is the pattern? What numbers go on the next two doors?*** Help children understand by asking: ***What do you know?*** The first 3 doors have 12, 14, and 16. Ask: ***What do you need to find?*** Find the pattern and what numbers go on the next two doors.
2. Help children plan and solve. Have them build a train of 12 snap cubes, all the same color. Ask: ***How can you change the train so it has 14 snap cubes, the number on the next door?*** Add 2 more snap cubes; Have children add two more snap cubes of a different color and count to make sure their trains have 14 cubes. Repeat to build the train to 16, using a third color. Ask: ***What is the pattern?*** Add two each time; Have children complete the pattern for the last two doors, using cubes if they like.
3. Help children look back and check by asking: ***How did you solve the problem?*** They used snap cubes to find the pattern and figure out what comes next.
4. Talk children through another problem similarly. Then have them complete the remaining problems.

Name ______________________

Look for a Pattern (continued)

Look for the pattern.
Write the missing numbers.

5. 4 6 8 10 ___

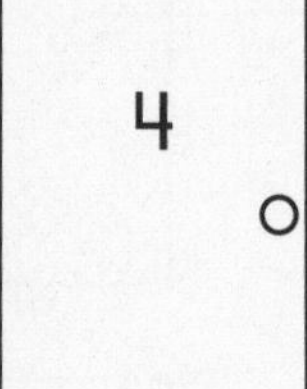

6. 40 35 30 ___ ___

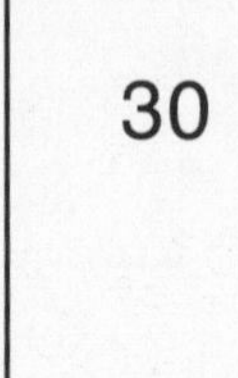
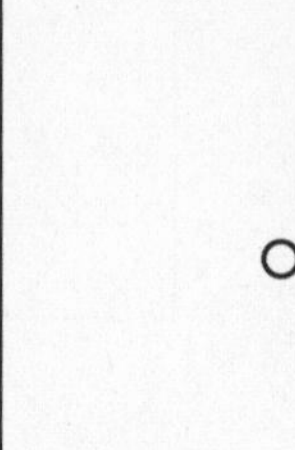

7. 28 30 32 ___ ___

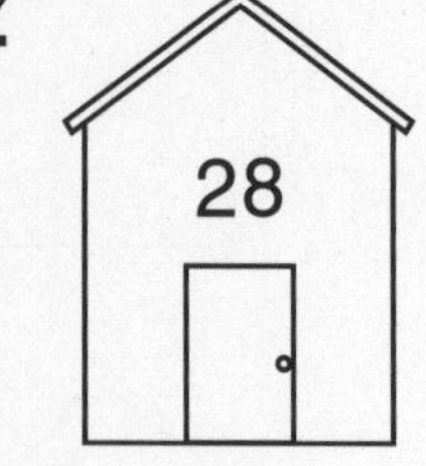
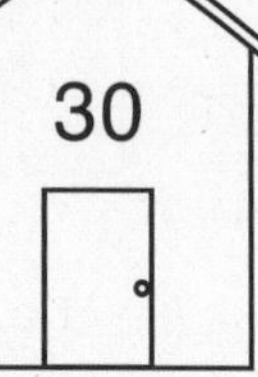
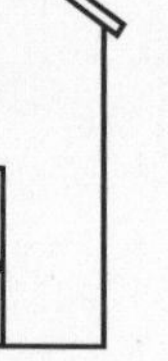
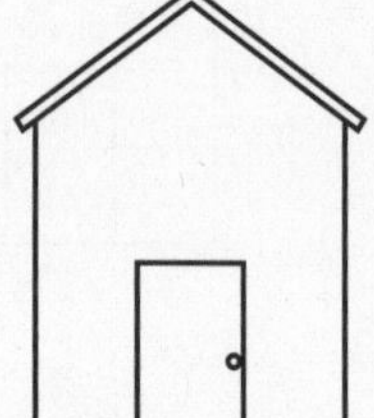
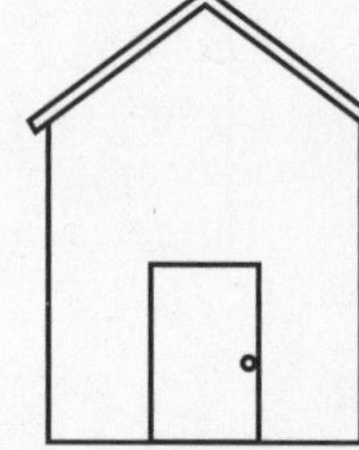

8. 70 60 50 ___ ___

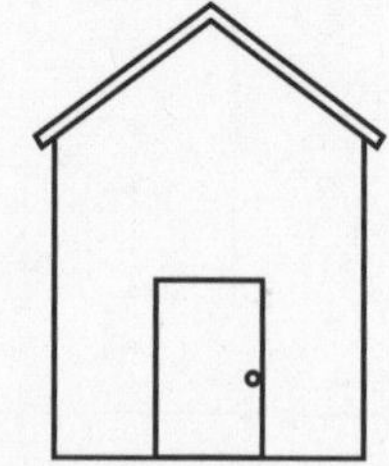
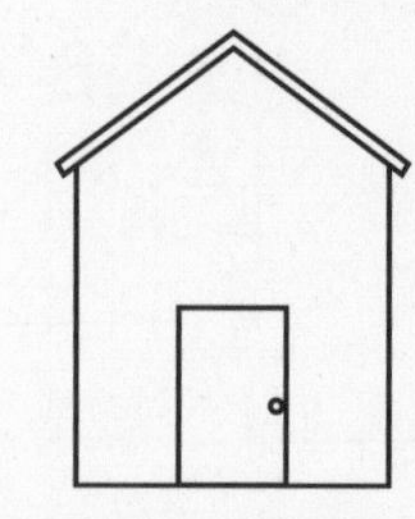

9. **Reasoning** Make your own pattern.

30 ___ ___ ___ ___

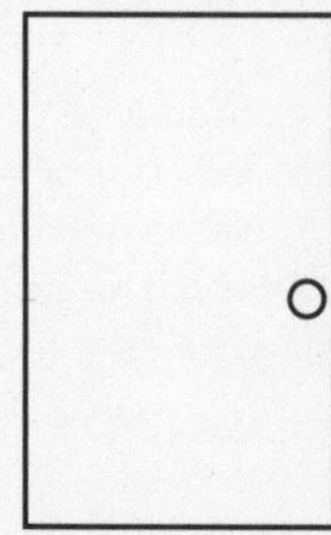
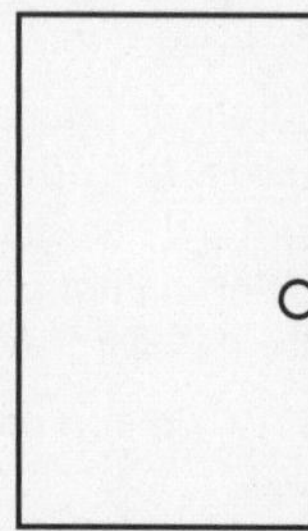
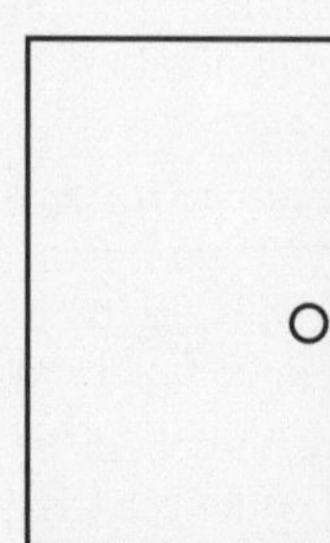
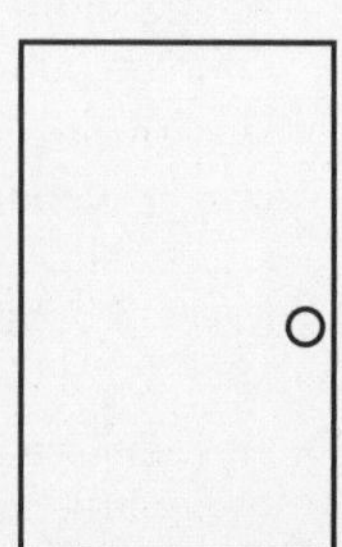

Name ______________________________

Look for a Pattern

1. Jana is making a necklace with two colors of beads. She uses 1 red bead, then 3 blue beads, then 5 yellow beads. If she continues this pattern with green and then orange beads, how many orange beads will she use?

1, 3, 5, ______, ______

Pattern: ______________________________

2. Mario had 4 football cards to start. The table shows how many he had after buying new packs. How many cards did he have after buying 5 packs?

Packs	Cards
1 pack	14
2 packs	24
3 packs	34
4 packs	44
5 packs	

Pattern: ______________________________

____

Materials: Crayons or markers

1. Read the problem to the children. Help them understand by asking: ***What do you know?*** Jana uses 1 red, then 3 blue, and then 5 yellow beads to make a necklace. Have children color the picture of the necklace to match the information in the problem. ***What else do you know?*** Jana will use green beads next and then orange beads. ***What do you need to find?*** Find how many orange beads she will use.
2. Help children plan and solve by asking: ***How many green beads will Jana use?*** Have children write 7. ***What color will Jana use after green?*** orange; ***How many orange beads will Jana use?*** Have children write 9.
3. Help children look back and check by asking: ***Did you answer the right question?*** Yes, Jana will use 9 orange beads. Ask: ***What is the pattern?*** Each new color uses two more beads. Have children write the pattern.
4. Do the other problem similarly.

Name ______________________________

Look for a Pattern (continued)

Find the pattern.
Write the missing numbers.

3. Ana's scarf has 2 parts yellow, then 5 parts green, then 8 parts orange. If it continues this pattern with white and then brown parts, how many brown parts does it have?

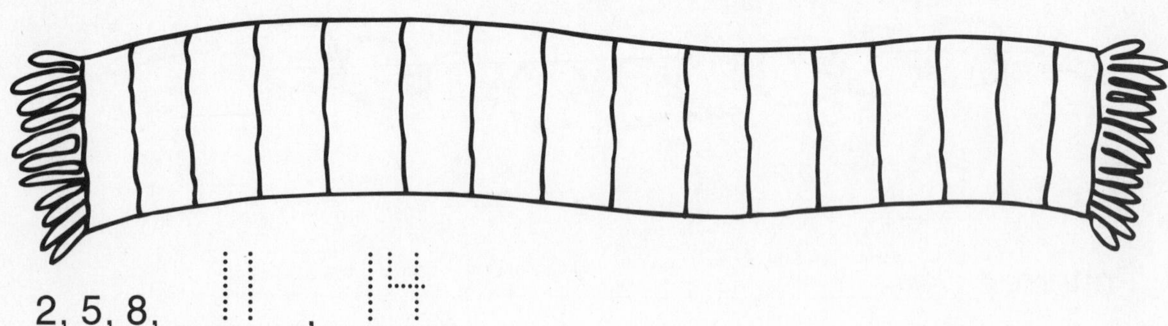

2, 5, 8, 11, 14

Pattern:

4. The table shows how many placemats children made each day at camp. If the pattern continued, how many placemats did they make on Friday?

Pattern:

Monday	6
Tuesday	16
Wednesday	26
Thursday	
Friday	

What comes next in each pattern?

5. 5, 9, 13, ______, ______

6. 4, 6, 8, ______, ______

7. 13, 23, 33, ______, ______

8. 26, 31, 36, ______, ______

Name ______________________________

Make a Table and Look for a Pattern

1. There are 5 bicycles in the yard.
Each bicycle has 2 wheels.
How many wheels are there in the yard altogether?

Number of Bicycles	1	2	3	4	
Number of Wheels	2	4			

There are ______ wheels in the yard altogether.

2. There are 4 boxes. Each box has 5 pencils.
How many pencils are there in all?

Number of Boxes	1	2		
Number of Pencils	5			

There are ______ pencils in all.

3. There are 3 monkeys.
Each monkey has 10 toes.
How many toes are there in all?

Number of Monkeys	1	2	3
Number of Toes	10		

There are ______ toes in all.

Materials: Snap cubes, 20 for each child

1. Read the problem to the children. Help them understand by asking: ***What do you know?*** There are 5 bicycles in the yard. Each bicycle has 2 wheels. ***What do you need to find?*** Find how many wheels there are in the yard altogether.
2. Help children plan and solve. Say: ***You can solve the problem by making a table to show a pattern. How many wheels does 1 bicycle have?*** 2 ***How many wheels do 2 bicycles have?*** 4 ***How many wheels do 3 bicycles have?*** 6. Then, have them complete the table, using snap cubes if necessary. Ask: ***How many wheels are there in the yard altogether?*** 10
3. Help children look back by asking: ***What was the pattern?*** Sample answer: Add two more wheels for each bicycle.
4. Do the other problems similarly.

Name ______________________________

Make a Table and Look for a Pattern (continued)

Find the pattern. Write the numbers.

4. There are 5 sheep. Each sheep gives 3 bags of wool. How many bags of wool in all?

Number of Sheep	1	2			
Number of Bags	3	6			

There are ______ bags of wool in all.

5. There are 4 cats. Each cat has 4 paws. How many paws in all?

Number of Cats	1			
Number of Paws	4			

The cats have ______ paws in all.

6. Reasoning If there are 5 cats, how many paws do they have altogether? ______________

Name ______________________________

Make a Table

1. How many different ways can Carlos put 4 balls in 2 boxes?

Box 1	Box 2
4	0
3	

There are ______ ways.

2. How many different ways can Trina put 5 balls in 2 boxes?

Box 1	Box 2
5	0

There are ______ ways.

Materials: Two half sheets of paper and 10 counters for each child

1. Read the problem and help children understand by asking: ***What do you know?*** Carlos wants to put 4 balls into 2 boxes. ***What do you need to find?*** Find how many ways Carlos can put 4 balls into 2 boxes.
2. Help children plan and solve by saying: ***You can solve the problem by making a table.*** Have children put 4 counters on one sheet of paper and ask: ***What is one way Carlos can put 4 balls in 2 boxes?*** Have children trace 4 and 0 in the table. Then, have them move one counter to the other sheet of paper and ask: ***What is another way Carlos can put 4 balls in 2 boxes?*** Have children trace 3 and write 1 in the table. Continue until children complete the table, moving one counter at a time. Ask: ***How many ways can Carlos put 4 balls into 2 boxes?*** Have children write 5.
3. Help children look back and check by asking: ***How do we know we have all the possible ways?*** The first box can only have 4, 3, 2, 1, or 0 balls. Do the other problem similarly.

Name ______________________________

Make a Table (continued)

3. Latisha wants to give 3 bottles of juice to her friends. How many different choices of juice does Latisha have?

Fill in the table to solve the problem.

Apple Juice	Grape Juice	Orange Juice
3	0	0
2	1	
2		1
1		0
1	1	
1		
0		0
	2	
		2

Latisha has ______ choices.

Name ____________________

Use Objects

1. Keisha has 6 marbles.
$\frac{1}{2}$ of her marbles are blue.
How many marbles are blue?

$\frac{1}{2}$ of 6 = 3

2. Keisha has 6 marbles.
$\frac{1}{3}$ of Keisha's marbles are yellow.
How many marbles are yellow?

$\frac{1}{3}$ of 6 = ______

3. Li has 6 marbles.
$\frac{2}{3}$ of his marbles are red.
How many marbles are red?

$\frac{2}{3}$ of 6 = ______

Materials: Crayons or markers, 12 two-color counters for each child

1. Read the problem to the children. Help them understand by asking: ***What do you know?*** Keisha has 6 marbles. $\frac{1}{2}$ of her marbles are blue. ***What do you need to find?*** Find how many of Keisha's marbles are blue.
2. Help children plan and solve by saying: ***You can solve the problem by using objects.*** Have children show 6 counters for Keisha's 6 marbles. Then have them put the counters into 2 equal sized groups. Have children circle two groups of marbles on their paper to match the counters. Say: ***Each group is half of Keisha's marbles.*** Have children color one group of marbles on their paper. Ask: ***How many of Keisha's marbles are blue?*** Have children write 3.
3. Help children look back and check by asking: ***How did objects help you solve the problem?*** Sample answer: The objects made it easier to divide the counters into 2 equal groups.
4. Do the other problems similarly. For item 3, have children divide the counters into 3 equal groups and color 2 of the groups.

Name ________________________________

Use Objects (continued)

Use counters to solve.

4. Jim has 8 apples.
$\frac{1}{2}$ of his apples are red.
How many of Jim's apples are red?

$\frac{1}{2}$ of 8 = 4

5. Lisa has 8 apples.
$\frac{3}{4}$ of her apples are red.
How many of Lisa's apples are red?

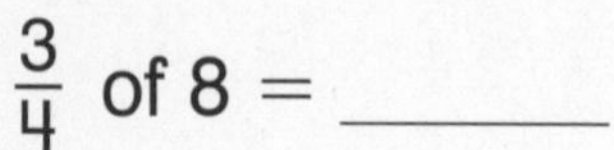

$\frac{3}{4}$ of 8 = ______

6. Vero has 9 apples.
$\frac{2}{3}$ of her apples are red.
How many of Vero's apples are red?

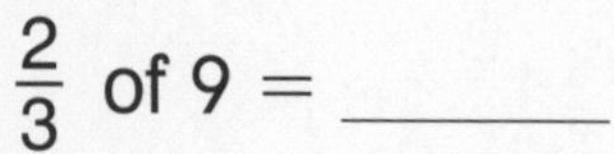

$\frac{2}{3}$ of 9 = ______

7. Al has 12 apples.
$\frac{1}{4}$ of his apples are red.
How many of Al's apples are red?

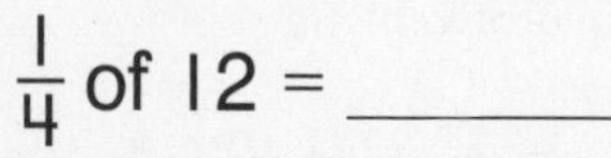

$\frac{1}{4}$ of 12 = ______

Name ______________________________

Act It Out

1. Sue has 5 bells.
Tim has 6 bells.
Caro has 3 bells.

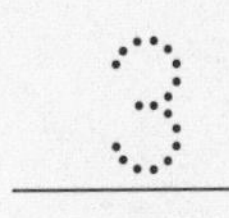  

___	___	___
least	between	most

Who has the most bells? Tim

Who has the least bells? __________

2. Will has 8 toy cars.
Joe has 5 toy cars.
Patty has 7 toy cars.

___	___	___
least	between	most

Who has the most toy cars? __________

Who has the least toy cars? __________

Materials: Snap cubes, 21 for each child

1. Read the problem to the children. Help them understand by asking: ***What do you know?*** Sue has 5 bells. Tim has 6 bells. Caro has 3 bells. ***What do you need to find?*** Find who has the most bells and who has the least.
2. Help children plan and solve by saying: ***You can solve the problem by acting out the problem with snap cubes.*** Have children make a train of 5 snap cubes for Sue's bells, a train of 6 snap cubes for Tim's bell, and a train of 3 snap cubes for Caro's bells.
3. Have children arrange the trains in order from the one with the least snap cubes to the one with the most. Ask: ***How many cubes are in the train with the least?*** Have children trace 3 above the line with least. Ask: ***How many cubes are in the train with the most?*** Have children trace 6 above the line with most. ***How many cubes are in the train that is between 3 and 6?*** Have children trace 5 above the line with between. Say: ***Six was the most. Who had 6 bells?*** Have children trace Tim. ***Three was the least. Who had 3 bells?*** Have children write Caro.
4. Help children look back and check by saying: ***Did you answer the right question?*** yes
5. Do the other problem similarly.

Name ______________________

Act It Out (continued)

Use the cubes to act out the story.
Write the numbers from least to greatest.
Answer the questions.

Some children collect leaves.

3. Ana has 6 leaves.
Jay has 9 leaves.
Tom has 5 leaves.

_____ _____ 9
least between most

Who has the most leaves? __________

Who has the least leaves? __________

4. Kay has 7 leaves.
Mark has 4 leaves.
Lee has 10 leaves.

_____ _____ _____
least between most

Who has the most leaves? __________

Who has the least leaves? __________

5. Min has 3 leaves.
Wendy has 8 leaves.
Patty has 6 leaves.

_____ _____ _____
least between most

Who has the most leaves? __________

Who has the least leaves? __________

Name ______________________________

Make an Organized List

1. Find 4 ways you can make this shape using pattern blocks.

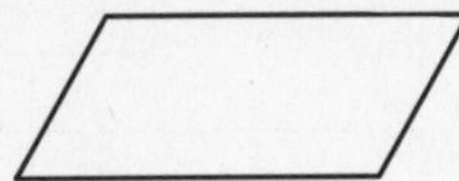

These are the same way.

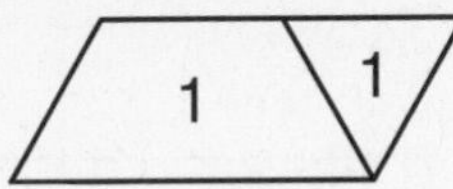

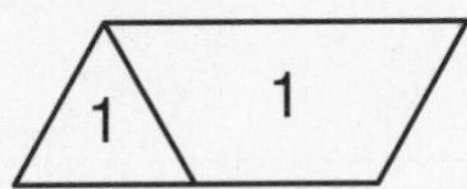

Ways to Make (parallelogram)			
Shapes I used	trapezoid	rhombus	triangle
Way 1	1	0	1
Way 2			
Way 3			
Way 4			

Materials: Pattern blocks, including 1 hexagon, 2 trapezoids, 1 parallelogram, 3 rhombuses, and 6 triangles for each pair, or group

1. Read the problem to the children. Help them understand by asking: ***What do you need to find?*** Find 3 different ways to make the pattern block shown using other pattern blocks. Show children how to put the trapezoid and triangle on top of the parallelogram block. Tell them this is one way to make the block. Then, have children turn the blocks (not pick them up and rearrange them) so they look like the other combination shown above. Ask: ***Are these the same way to show the block or is this a different way?*** It is the same way.
2. Help children plan and solve by saying: ***You can solve by making an organized list. You made the block using one of these*** (hold up trapezoid) ***and one of these*** (hold up triangle)***, so put a 1 under each of these shapes in the list.*** Have children trace the 1, 0, and 1 in the first row of the table.
3. Have children work together to find 3 other ways to make the shape and complete the table.
4. Help children look back and check by saying: ***Did you find 4 different ways?*** Discuss the ways the children found and how they recorded the ways in the table.

Name ______________________________

Make an Organized List (continued)

2. Use pattern blocks. How many ways can you make this shape? Record the blocks you used.

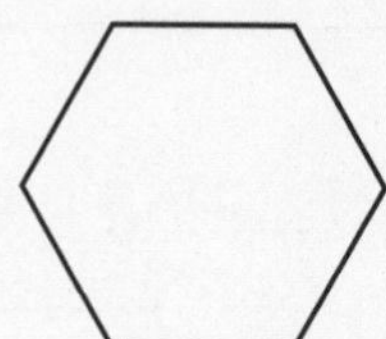

Ways to Make				
Shapes I used				
Way 1	1	0	0	0
Way 2	0			
Way 3	0			
Way 4	0			
Way 5	0			
Way 6	0			
Way 7	0			
Way 8	0			

How many ways can you make a hexagon? __________

Name ______________________

Try, Check, and Revise

Maddie bought 2 items.
Together they cost 10¢.
Which items did she buy?

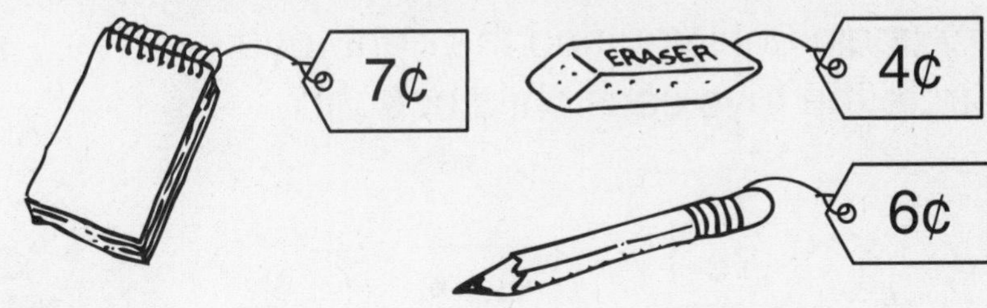

1. Try: and

Check: ___7___ ¢ + ______ ¢ = ______ ¢

Too high Right Too low

2. Try: and

Check: ______ ¢ + ______ ¢ = ______ ¢

Too high Right Too low

3.

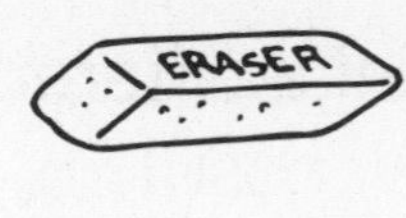

1. Read the problem to the children. Help them understand by asking: ***What do you know?*** Maddie bought 2 items. The two items together cost 10 cents. ***What do you know from looking at the picture?*** An eraser costs 4 cents. A notebook costs 7 cents. A pencil costs 6 cents. ***What do you need to find?*** Find which items Maddie bought.
2. Help children plan and solve by saying: ***You can solve the problem by using Try, Check, and Revise. First, you choose 2 items that might be the ones Maddie bought. Let's choose the notebook and the eraser. How much does a notebook cost?*** Have children trace the 7. ***How much does an eraser cost?*** Have children write 4. ***How much do they cost in all?*** Have children write 11.
3. Ask: ***Is 11 cents too high, too low, or just right?*** Have children circle "Too high." ***Since 11 cents is too high, revise your guess by choosing a cheaper item in place of one item you guessed the first time. Try the pencil instead of the notebook.*** Have children try these two items as they tried the first guess. Ask: ***Is 10 cents too high, too low, or just right?*** Have children circle "Right." Ask: ***Which two items did Maddie buy?*** Have children circle the pencil and the eraser.
4. Help children look back and check by asking: ***How do you know your answer is correct?*** The two items cost 10 cents.

Name ______________________________

Try, Check, and Revise (continued)

Guess which toys each child bought.
Write a number sentence to check your guess.
Try again until you find the right toys.
Circle the toys each child bought.

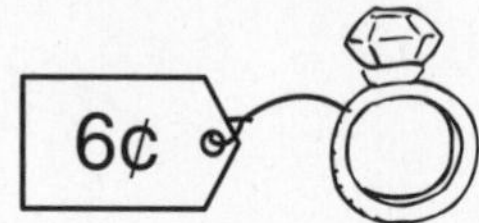

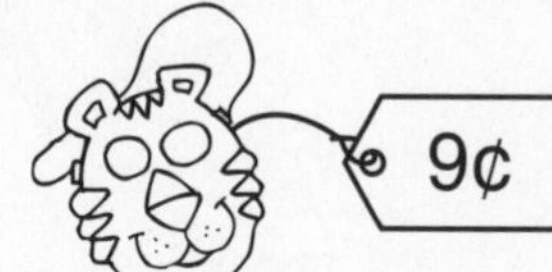

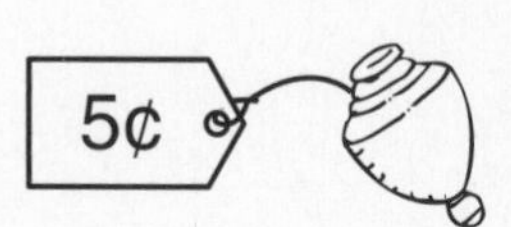

4. Javier bought 2 different toys.
Together they cost 11¢

Try: ______ ¢ + ______ ¢ = ______ ¢

Try: ______ ¢ + ______ ¢ = ______ ¢

Try: ______ ¢ + ______ ¢ = ______ ¢

5. May-Li bought 2 different toys.
Together they cost 16¢

Try: ______ ¢ + ______ ¢ = ______ ¢

Try: ______ ¢ + ______ ¢ = ______ ¢

Try: ______ ¢ + ______ ¢ = ______ ¢

Name ____________________

Use Objects and Reasoning

1. How much does it hold?

2. How tall is it?

3. How heavy is it?

4. How wide is it?

Materials: A quart juice carton, a paper clip, a balance scale, and a measuring cup

1. Show the juice carton. Ask: ***What is the best tool to use to measure how much juice it holds?*** Have children circle the measuring cup.
2. Say: ***Circle the best tool to use to measure how tall the carton is.*** paper clip
3. Say: ***Circle the best tool to use to measure how heavy the carton is.*** balance scale
4. Say: ***Circle the best tool to use to measure how wide the carton is.*** paper clip

Name ______________________________

Use Objects and Reasoning (continued)

Circle the best tool to use for each measurement.

5. How long is it?

6. How much does it hold?

7. How heavy is it?

8. How tall is it?

9. **Reasoning** What other measurement can be made of the milk carton? What tool would you use?

Name ______________________________

Use Reasoning

1. Which shape am I?
I have 4 sides.
The lengths of all my sides are equal.

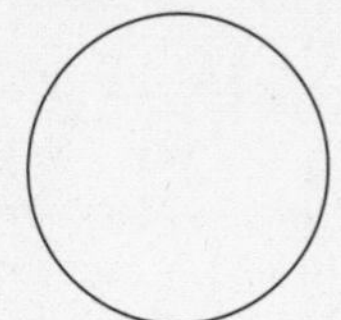   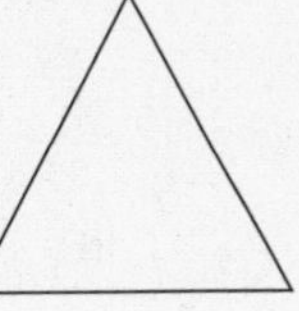

2. Which shape am I?
I have flat surfaces.
If you trace my flat surface, you make a square.
I have less than 6 sides.

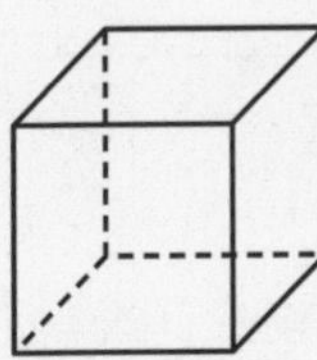 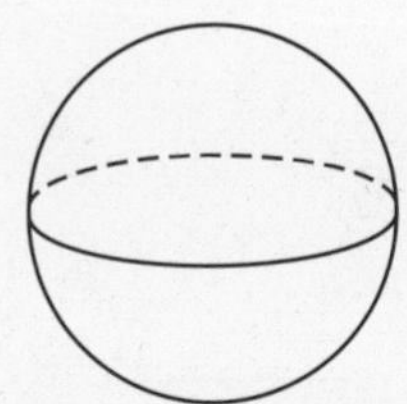 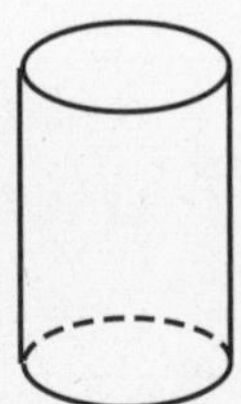 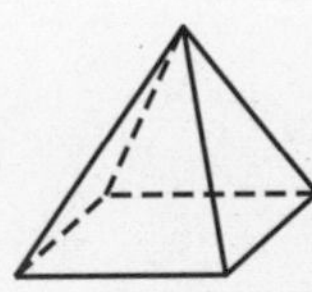

3. Which shape am I?
I do not have any vertices.
I have 0 flat surfaces.

 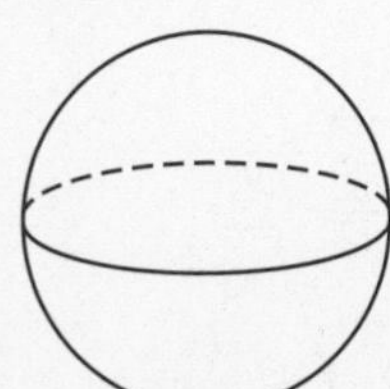 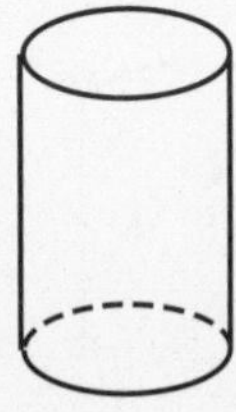 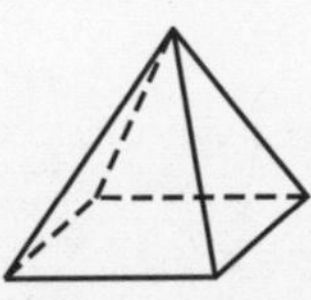

Materials: Geometric solids for demonstration

1. Read the problem to the children. Help them understand by asking: ***What do you know?*** The shape has 4 sides. The lengths of all the sides are equal. ***What do you need to find?*** Find which shape fits the clues.
2. Help children plan and solve by saying: ***You can solve the problem by using reasoning. Does a circle have 4 sides?*** Have children cross out the circle. ***Which other shape does NOT have 4 sides?*** Have children cross out the triangle. ***Are the lengths of all the sides of a rectangle the same length?*** Have children cross out the rectangle. ***Does a square have 4 sides?*** yes ***Are the lengths of all the sides of a square the same length?*** Have children circle the square.
3. Help children look back and check by asking: ***How did you use reasoning to solve the problem?*** Sample answer: Cross out each shape that doesn't fit the clues until only one is left.
4. Do the other problems similarly, showing each solid as you discuss it.

Name ______________________________

Use Reasoning (continued)

Cross out the shapes that do not fit the clues.
Circle the shape that answers the question.

4. Which shape am I?
I have more than 3 sides.
I have 4 vertices.

 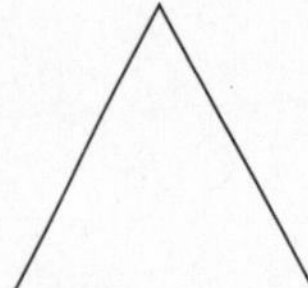 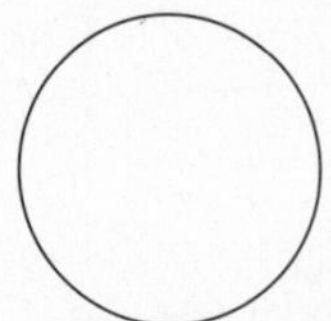 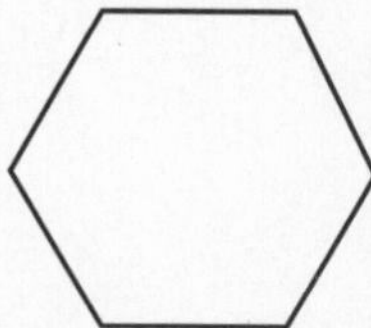

5. Which shape am I?
I have fewer than 6 sides.
The lengths of all my sides are equal.

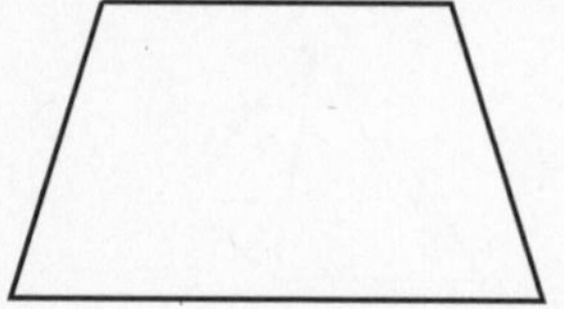 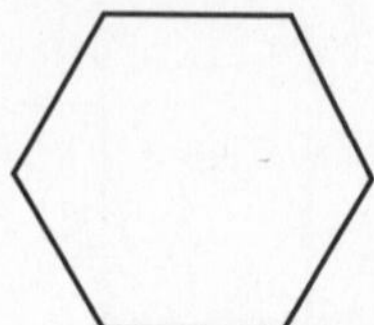 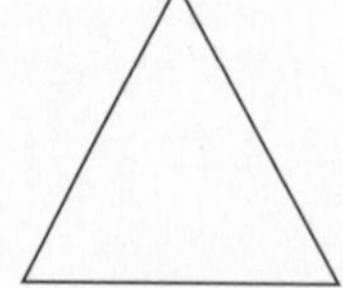 

6. Which shape am I?
If you trace my flat surface, you make a circle.
I have 2 flat surfaces.

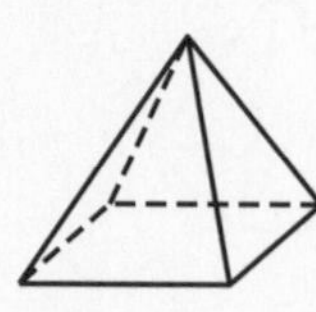 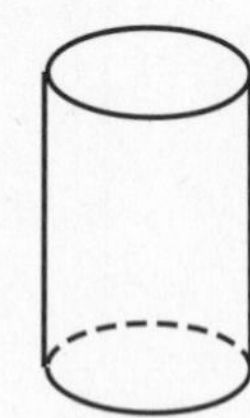  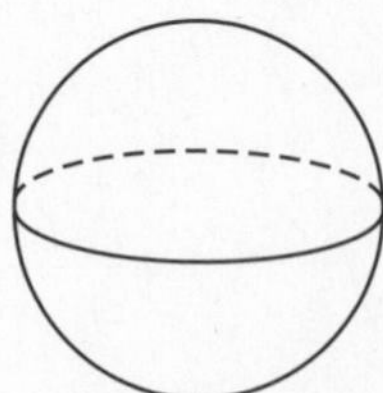

7. Which shape am I?
I have 8 vertices.
If you trace any of my flat surfaces, you make a square.

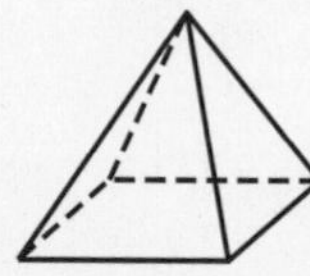 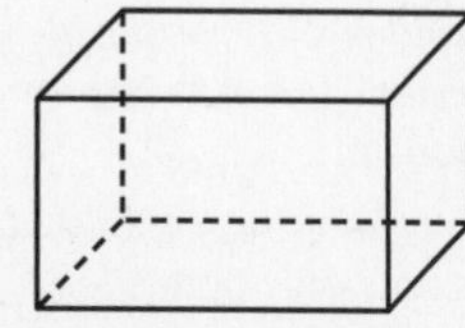 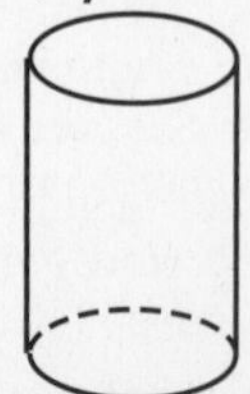 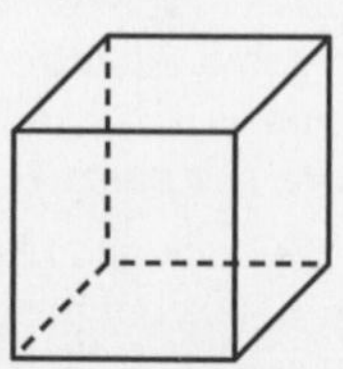

Name ______________________________

Draw a Picture and Write a Number Sentence

1. Rico has 5 stickers.
He gets 2 more stickers.
How many stickers does he have in all?

5 ○ 2 = 7

7 stickers in all

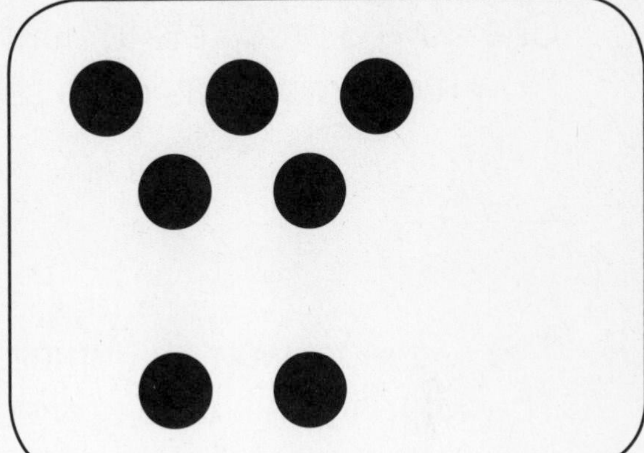

2. Maria has 6 stickers.
She gives 3 stickers to Dani.
How many stickers does Maria have left?

6 ○ 3 = ______

______ stickers left

1. Read the problem to the children. Help them understand by asking: ***What do you know?*** Rico has 5 stickers. Rico gets 2 more stickers. ***What do you need to find?*** Find how many stickers Rico has in all.
2. Help children plan and solve by saying: ***You can solve the problem by drawing a picture and writing a number sentence. To find how many stickers Rico has in all, do you need to add or subtract?*** Have children write a plus sign in the circle. Ask: ***What do you need to add?*** Have children trace 5 and 2. Have children draw a picture of circles to show the problem and to find 5 + 2. Ask: ***What is 5 plus 2?*** Have children write 7. ***How many stickers does Rico have in all?*** Have children write 7.
3. Help children look back and check by asking: ***What is your number sentence?*** 5 + 2 = 7
4. Do the other problem similarly. Have children draw circles and then cross them out for the picture.

Name ______________________________

Draw a Picture and Write a Number Sentence (continued)

Write a number sentence.
Draw a picture and solve.

3. Marcia made 7 bracelets.
She gave 3 bracelets to her friends.
How many bracelets does she have left.

7 ◯ 3 ◯ 4 ______ bracelets

4. The red team won 12 games.
The white team won 8 games.
How many more games did the red team win?

______ ◯ ______ ◯ ______ ______ games

Use the table to help you solve Exercises 5 and 6.

Players	Game 1	Game 2
Harvey	5	7
Juanita	8	4

5. How many points did Harvey score altogether in Games 1 and 2?

______ ◯ ______ ◯ ______ points

6. How many more points did Juanita score in Game 1 than Harvey?

______ ◯ ______ ◯ ______ points

Name ______________________

Draw a Picture and Write a Number Sentence

1. How many apples in all?

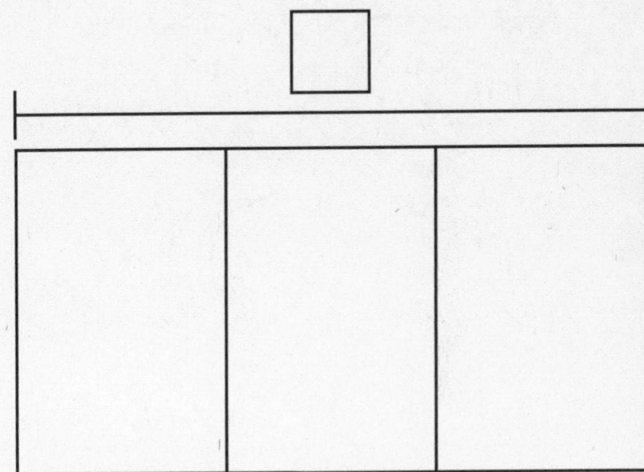

3 ⊗ 5 = ______

2. How many cherries in all?

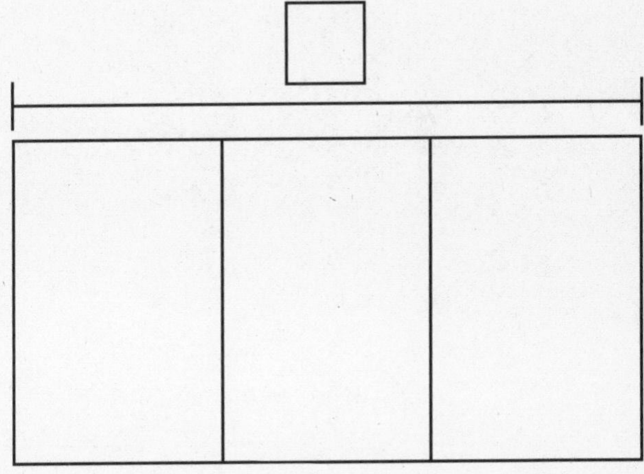

______ ◯ ______ = ______

1. Read the problem to the children. Help them understand by asking: ***What do you know?*** There are 3 baskets. There are 5 apples in each basket ***What do you need to find?*** Find how many apples in all.
2. Help children plan and solve by saying: ***You can solve by drawing a picture and writing a number sentence. Are all the groups the same size?*** yes; Have children draw circles in the model to show the 3 groups of 5. ***Since all the groups are the same size, you can multiply. How many groups are there?*** Have children trace 3. ***How many are in each group?*** Have children trace 5. ***How many apples in all?*** Have children write 15 in the number sentence and in the model.
3. Help children look back and check by asking: ***What is your number sentence?*** 3 × 5 = 15
4. Do the other problem similarly, asking how many rows and how many in each row.

Name ______________________________

Draw a Picture and Write a Number Sentence (continued)

Draw a picture and write a number sentence.
Solve.

3. How many bananas in all?

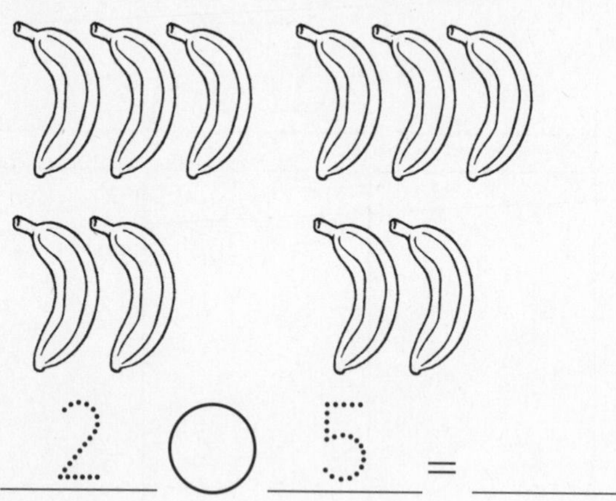

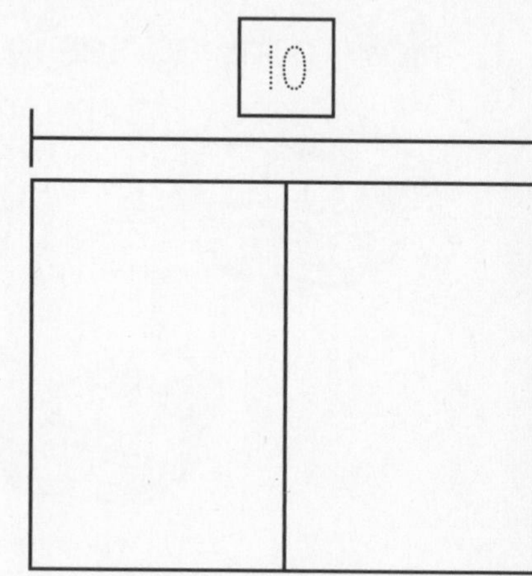

2 ○ 5 = ____

4. How many shells in all?

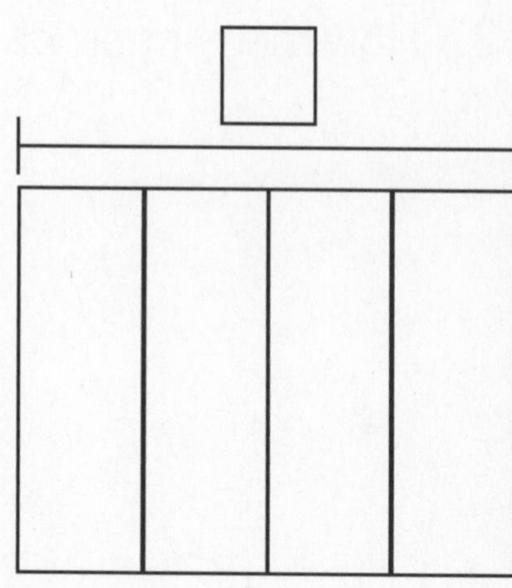

____ ○ ____ = ____

5. How many stars in all?

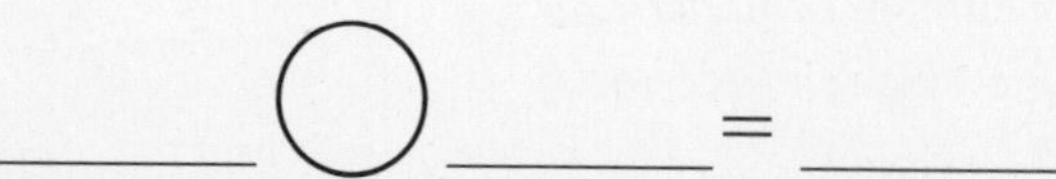

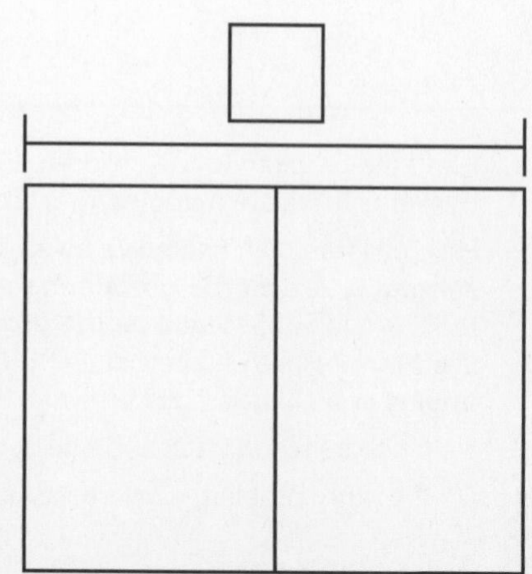

____ ○ ____ = ____

Name ______________________________

Make a Table and Look for a Pattern

Ann and Jane began reading the same book on the same day. If Ann reads 8 pages each day and Jane reads 5 pages each day, what page will Jane read on the day that Ann reads page 40?

Solve by answering 1 to 6.

Answer 1 and 2 to **understand** the problem.

1. What do you know from reading the problem?

Ann reads _______ pages each day.

Jane reads _______ pages each day.

They started the same day.

2. What do you need to find?

Answer 3 to 5 to **plan and solve** the problem.

You can solve the problem by making a table and looking for a pattern.

3. Use patterns to complete the table below.

Day	**1**	**2**	**3**	**4**	**5**	**6**
Ann's Page	8	16				
Jane's Page	5					

4. What day will Ann read page 40? ___________

5. What page will Jane read on the day Ann reads page 40? ___________

Name ______________________

Make a Table and Look for a Pattern (continued)

Answer 6 to **look back** at your solution.

6. Did you answer the right question? ______

Use patterns to complete each table. Solve each problem.

7. Rebecca must put 4 eggs in each basket. There are 8 baskets. How many eggs does she need? ______

Number of Baskets	1	2	3	4	5	6	7	8
Number of Eggs	4	8						

8. Martin needs to water each tree with 3 gallons of water. How many gallons of water will he need for 7 trees?

Number of trees	1	2	3	4	5	6	7
Gallons of water							

____

9. Diego recorded the height of a bean plant. The first week, the plant was 2 inches high. The second, third, and fourth week, it was 4 inches, 6 inches, and 8 inches high. At this rate, when will the bean plant be 12 inches high?

Week	1	2	3	4	5	6	7
Height							

____

10. Each quilt square has 2 red sections and 3 blue sections. If 18 blue sections are used, how many red sections are needed?

squares						
red sections						
blue sections						

____

Name ___________________________

Act It Out

Materials color tiles, 16 for each student

Jada bought balloons for the party. She bought red, yellow, and blue balloons. She bought at least one of each color. Use the information at the right to find how many balloons of each color she bought.

Balloons Jada Bought
7 yellow 3 more red than blue 16 balloons in all

Solve by answering 1 to 6.

Answer 1 to 3 to **understand** the problem.

1. What do you know from reading the problem?

Jada bought ________, ________, and ________ balloons.

2. What do you know from reading the chart?

Jada bought ________ yellow balloons.

Jada bought ________ more red balloons than blue balloons.

Jada bought ________ balloons in all.

3. What do you need to find?

Answer 4 and 5 to **plan and solve** the problem.

You can solve the problem by acting out the problem with color tiles.

4. Count out 16 tiles. Separate 7 of them for the yellow balloons. How many red and blue balloons did Jada buy? ________

Name ______________________________

Act It Out (continued)

5. Separate the tiles representing the red and blue balloons into two piles, so one pile has 3 more tiles than the other. How many balloons of each color did Jada buy?

_______ yellow _______ red _______ blue

Answer 6 to **check** your solution.

6. Reasoning Explain why your answer is correct.

Solve each problem.

7. Min is playing with modeling clay. To try to protect the table, his mother put down a plastic placemat. The placemat had 40 small squares on it. How many squares were in each row?

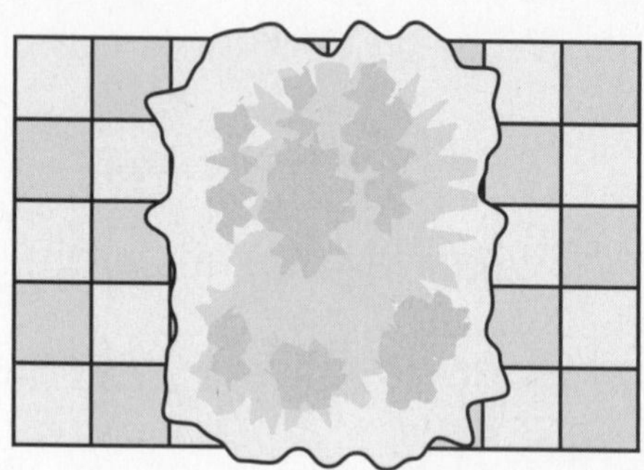

____

8. There are 17 entries in the photo contest. The photos consist of animal photos, nature photos, and portraits. There are 5 portraits. There are 6 fewer nature photos than animal photos. How many of each type of photo was in the contest?

____

9. Tim bought 18 apples for the apple-bobbing contest. He bought red, yellow, and green apples. There are 3 yellow apples. There are twice as many red apples as green apples. How many of each color apple did he buy?

____

Name ______________________________

Make an Organized List

Materials 4 index cards cut in half to make 8 halves

Veronica is playing a game called *Guess the Number*. What are all the possible numbers that fit the clues shown on the right? How many numbers are there?

Solve by answering 1 to 10.

Clues
It is a 3-digit odd number.
The hundreds digit is less than 3.
The tens digit is greater than 6.
The ones digit is greater than 6.

Answer 1 to 5 to **understand** the problem.

1. What do you know from reading the problem?

The number has ______ digits and is ____________.

The hundreds digit is less than ______.

Both the tens and ones digits are greater than ______.

2. What do you need to find?

3. What digits can be in the hundreds place? ____________

4. What digits can be in the tens place? ____________

5. What digits can be in the ones place? ____________

Answer 6 to 9 to **plan and solve** the problem.

6. Write the possible digits for each place on index cards.

Name ______________________________

Make an Organized List (continued)

You can solve the problem by making an organized list.

7. Put the cards with the smallest digits for each place together. What is one possible number?

____

This number is first in the list at the right.

8. Change the card for the ones digit and write another number in the list at the right. When you use all the ones cards, change the tens digit card to the next highest digit and match it with each possible ones digit. Continue in this organized way until you have listed all the possible numbers.

9. How many numbers are possible? _______

Hundreds	Tens	Ones
1	7	7

Answer 10 to **look back** at how you solved the problem.

10. Did you answer the right question? _______

Complete each list to solve.

11. The cups used to sell drinks at the game come in packages of 100 or 10. How many different ways can 320 cups be bought?

____

Packages of 100	Packages of 10
2	12

12. You have black pants and tan pants. You have 3 shirts: black, red, and green. How many different outfits can you make?

B–B _______________

B–R _______________

B–G _______________

Name ______________________________

Try, Check, and Revise

The Koch family bought 5 tickets at the prices shown on the sign at the right. They spent $36. How many tickets of each type did they buy?

TICKETS	
Adults	$9 each
Children	$6 each

Solve by answering 1 to 8.

Answer 1 to 3 to **understand** the problem.

1. What do you know from reading the problem?

The Koch family bought ________ tickets and spent ________.

2. What do you know from reading the sign?

Adult's tickets cost ________ and children's tickets cost ________.

3. What do you need to find?

Answer 4 to 7 to **plan and solve** the problem.

You can solve the problem by using the strategy Try, Check, and Revise.

4. Suppose you guess that the Koch family bought 3 adult and 2 children's tickets. Check your guess. How much do 3 adult's and 2 children's tickets cost? ________

5. Is the cost too high, too low, or just right? ____________

6. How can you change your guess to get a lower total?

7. Revise the guess and try again until the total cost is $36. How many tickets of each type did the Koch family buy?

Name ______________________________

Try, Check, and Revise (continued)

Answer 8 to **look back** at how you solved the problem.

8. Explain how to use Try, Check, and Revise to solve a problem.

For Exercises 9 to 11, use the table at the right.

Camping Town	
Sleeping bag	$10
Flashlight	$3
Lantern	$5
Canteen	$4
Dried food	$2

9. Karen bought 2 different items. She spent $8. Which items did she buy?

____

10. Jake bought 3 different items. He spent a total of $15. Which items did he buy?

____

11. Adam spent $19 at Camping Town on 4 items. Two of his items were the same. What did he buy?

____

Solve each problem.

12. Gina has twice as many goldfish as zebra fish. Together, there are 42 of these two types of fish in her tank. How many goldfish and zebra fish does she have?

____

13. Josh delivers pizza. In his money pouch are 6 bills worth $18. If he only has $1 and $5 bills, how many of each bill does he have?

____

Name ______________________________

Draw a Picture and Write a Number Sentence

The Bulldogs basketball team scored 38 points in the first half of the game. In the second half of the game the team scored 46 points. How many points did the Bulldogs score in the entire game?

Solve by answering 1 to 7.

Answer 1 and 2 to **understand** the problem.

1. What do you know from reading the problem?

The Bulldogs scored _______ points in the first half of the game.

The Bulldogs scored _______ points in the second half of the game.

2. What do you need to find?

Answer 3 to 6 to **plan and solve** the problem.

You can solve the problem by drawing a picture and writing a number sentence.

3. Complete the picture at the right to show what you know.

?

4. You know both parts and need to find the total. Do you add or subtract?

____

5. Write a number sentence to solve. ____________________

6. How many points did the Bulldogs score in the entire game? ______ points

Name ___________________________________

Draw a Picture and Write a Number Sentence (continued)

Answer 7 to **look back** at how you solved the problem.

7. Reasoning Use estimation to explain why your answer is reasonable.

8. How many more points did the Bulldogs score in the second half than in the first half? Complete the picture at the right and write a number sentence to solve.

46

Number sentence: ____________________ _______ more points

Draw a picture and write a number sentence to solve each problem.

9. There are 17 Asian elephants and 12 African elephants in the zoo. What is the total number of elephants in the zoo?

Number sentence: ____________________ _______ elephants

10. Maggie wants to buy a set of paints for her art class. The cost of the paints is $49. She has saved $17 from her allowance so far. How much more money does she need to buy the set of paints?

Number sentence: ____________________ $_______ more

11. The McKay family needs to drive 212 miles to reach the beach for a family vacation. If they have traveled 85 miles, how many more miles do they need to travel?

Number sentence: ____________________ _______ more miles

Name ______________________________

Draw a Picture and Write a Number Sentence

For the science project, Ms. Trapp needs 27 paper towel rolls for each of her 3 classes. How many rolls does she need in all?

Solve by answering 1 to 7.

Answer 1 and 2 to **understand** the problem.

1. What do you know from reading the problem?

Ms. Trapp needs _______ paper towel rolls for each class.

Ms. Trapp has _______ classes.

2. What do you need to find?

Answer 3 to 5 to **plan and solve** the problem.

You can solve the problem by drawing a picture and writing a number sentence.

3. Complete the picture at the right to show what you know.

? paper towel rolls

Paper towel rolls needed for each

4. Write a number sentence to solve.

____

5. How many paper towel rolls does Ms. Trapp need in all?

_______ paper towel rolls

Answer 6 and 7 to **look back and check** how you solved the problem.

6. Did you answer the right question? _______

Name ______________________________

Draw a Picture and Write a Number Sentence (continued)

7. Reasoning Use estimation to explain why your answer is reasonable.

Draw a picture and write a number sentence to solve each problem.

8. The catering company ordered 16 tablecloths. They also ordered 8 times as many napkins. How many napkins did they order?

tablecloths [16]

napkins [| | | | | | |] 8 times as many

? napkins in all

Number sentence: ______________ ______ napkins

9. Mr. and Mrs. Gordon have 11 grandsons and 8 granddaughters. How many grandchildren do the Gordons have?

Number sentence: ______________ ______ grandchildren

10. Yul bought a case for his CDs. Each page in the case holds 4 CDs. The case has 24 pages. How many CDs can the case hold?

______ CDs in all

CDs on each page

Number sentence: ______________ ______ CDs

11. Amy and Todd have blown up 34 balloons for a birthday party. Amy has blown up 18 balloons. How many did Todd blow up?

Number sentence: ______________ ______ balloons

Name ______________________________

Draw a Picture and Write a Number Sentence

The pet store ordered 24 hamsters. They put the hamsters in 6 different cages. If each cage had the same number of hamsters, how many hamsters were put in each cage?

Solve by answering 1 to 6.

Answer 1 and 2 to **understand** the problem.

1. What do you know from reading the problem?

The pet store ordered ______ hamsters.

The pet store put the hamsters in ______ different cages, with the same number of hamsters in each cage.

2. What do you need to find?

Answer 3 to 5 to **plan and solve** the problem.

You can solve the problem by drawing a picture and writing a number sentence.

3. Complete the picture at the right to show what you know.

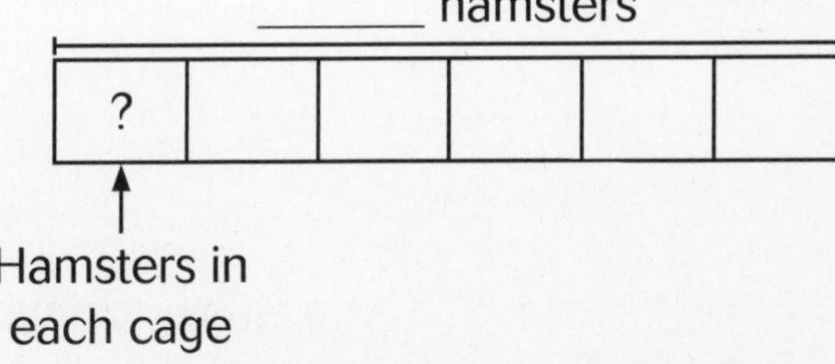

4. Write a number sentence to solve.

____

5. How many hamsters were put in each cage? ______ hamsters

Answer 6 to **look back** at how you solved the problem.

6. Did you answer the right question? ______

Name ______________________________

Draw a Picture and Write a Number Sentence (continued)

Draw a picture and write a number sentence to solve each problem.

7. The florist ordered 36 vases. The vases were packaged 4 to a box. How many boxes were delivered to the florist?

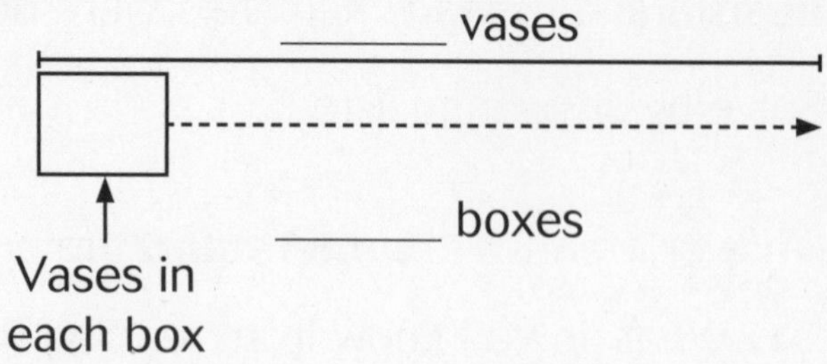

Number sentence:

____

______ boxes

______ vases

______ boxes

Vases in each box

8. Johnston has 6 rolls of quarters. Each roll has 40 quarters. How many quarters does Johnston have?

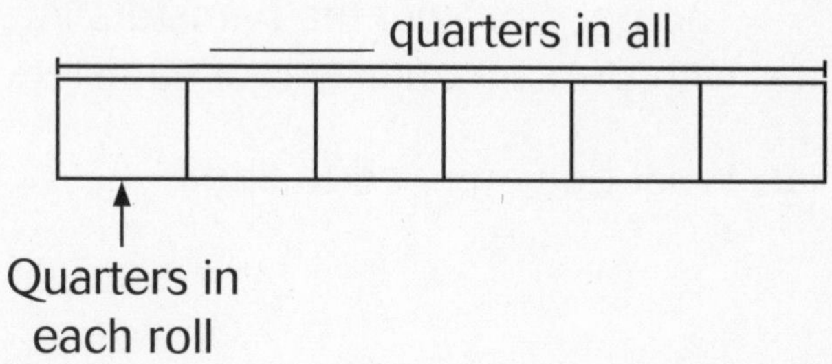

Number sentence:

____

______ quarters

______ quarters in all

Quarters in each roll

9. Coach Yellowstone ordered 40 basketballs. He put them in 5 different bins. If each bin had the same number of basketballs, how many basketballs were put in each bin?

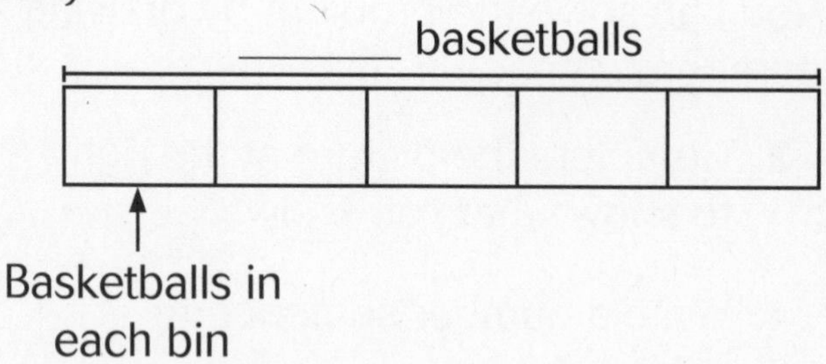

Number sentence:

____

______ basketballs

______ basketballs

Basketballs in each bin

10. Emily scored 7 times as many points on the video game as Roberta. Roberta scored 86 points. How many points did Emily score?

Number sentence:

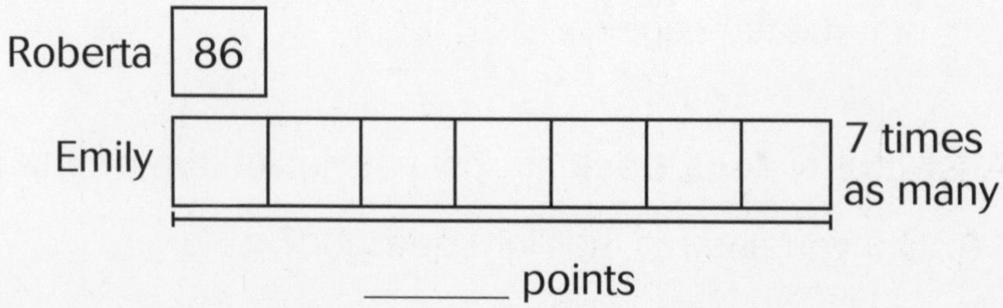

____

______ points

Roberta 86

Emily

7 times as many

______ points

Name ______________________________

Solve a Simpler Problem

A diagram of a flower garden in the city park is shown on the right. The garden is made of rose bushes and marigolds. The shaded part of the figure shows the part of the garden that is marigolds. What is the area of the shaded part of the flower garden?

Solve by answering 1 to 6.

Answer 1 and 2 to **understand** the problem.

1. What do you know from reading the problem?

The diagram shows a garden. The shaded part shows the part with marigolds.

The rest of the garden has ________.

2. What do you need to find?

Answer 3 to 5 to **plan and solve** the problem.

You can solve the problem by solving two simpler problems first.

3. What is the area of the whole garden?

_____ × _____ = _____

4. What is the area of the part that is not shaded?

_____ × _____ = _____

5. The area of the shaded part is the whole area minus the part that is not shaded. What is the area of the shaded part?

_____ − _____ = _____ square yards

Name ______________________________

Solve a Simpler Problem (continued)

Answer 6 to **look back** at how you solved the problem.

6. Explain how to use Solving a Simpler Problem to solve a problem.

Solve each problem.

Use the grid at the right for Exercises 7 and 8. Be careful, arrows show one-way streets.

7. Find the distance (the number of blocks) from home to the store and then to Grandma's.

____

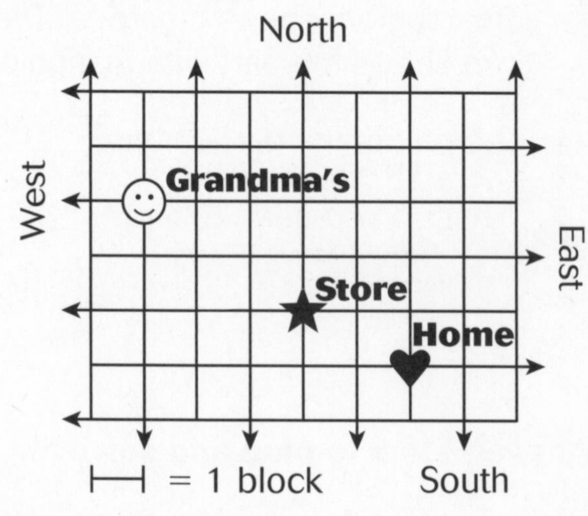

8. Sara started from home, drove 5 blocks north, 3 blocks west, and 4 blocks south, but she still needed to go to the store. How many blocks was she from the store?

____

Gloria tiled her bathroom floor. She used white and gray tiles as shown at the right. Use the diagram for Exercises 9 and 10.

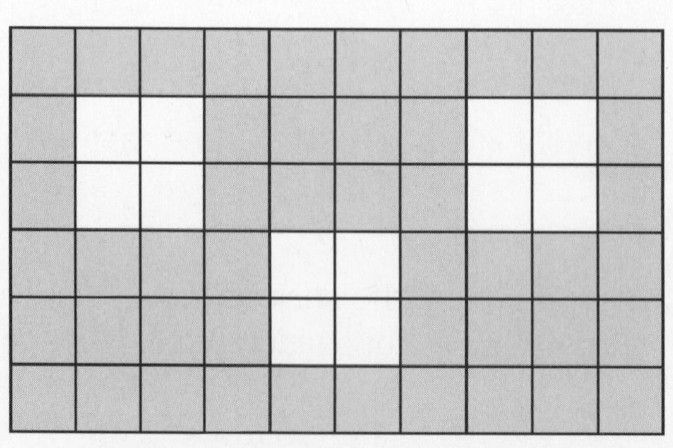

= 1 square foot

9. What is the gray area?

____

10. How much greater is the gray area than the white area?

____

Name ____

Make a Graph

Materials crayons or markers, grid paper

Students in two classes voted on the type of booth they would like to sponsor at the carnival. The results are in the tally charts below. Answer 1 to 4 to find which type of booth the two classes should sponsor together.

Mrs. Bentley's Class

Carnival Booth	Tally
Balloon Pop	𝍸 IIII
Ring Toss	𝍸 III
Face Painting	IIII

Mr. Chavez's Class

Carnival Booth	Tally
Balloon Pop	𝍸
Ring Toss	𝍸 III
Face Painting	𝍸 III

1. Draw a bar graph of each set of data.

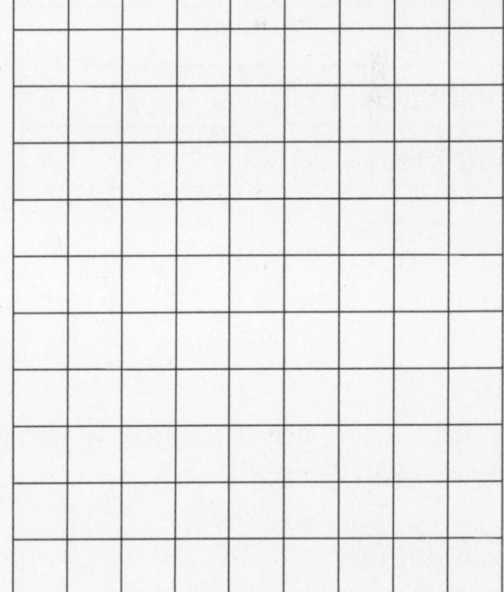

Name ______________________

Make a Graph (continued)

2. What was the least favorite type of booth of the students in Mrs. Bentley's Class? ______________

3. What was the least favorite type of booth of the students in Mr. Chavez's Class? ______________

4. **Reasoning** Which type of booth should the two classes sponsor together? Explain your choice.

Two classes voted on which type of seed they would like to plant in their garden. The results are shown in the tally charts below. Use the information in the tally charts for 5-8.

Ms. Aydin's Class

Type of Seed	Tally
Pumpkin	~~IIII~~ ~~IIII~~
Cantaloupe	~~IIII~~ II
Watermelon	~~IIII~~

Mr. Brown's Class

Type of Seed	Tally
Pumpkin	~~IIII~~ ~~IIII~~
Cantaloupe	IIII
Watermelon	~~IIII~~ III

5. Draw a horizontal bar graph of the results for each class. Use grid paper.

6. Which seed got the same number of votes from both classes? ______________

7. Cantaloupe got more votes from which class? ______________

8. **Reasoning** Was the favorite seed the same for both classes? Explain how you can tell from the graphs.

Name ______________________________

Work Backward

Between 4:00 P.M. and 5:00 P.M., the temperature dropped 4 degrees. Every hour after that, the temperature dropped 2 degrees. At 8:00 P.M., the temperature was 52°F. What was the temperature at 4:00 P.M.?

F
70
60
50
40
8:00 P.M.

Solve by answering 1 to 7.

Answer 1 and 2 to **understand** the problem.

1. What do you know from reading the problem?

The temperature dropped ______ degrees, between 4:00 P.M. and 5:00 P.M.

The temperature dropped ______ degrees, every hour after 5:00 P.M.

The temperature was ______, at 8:00 P.M.

2. What do you need to find?

____

Answer 3 to 5 to **plan and solve** the problem.

You can solve by working backward.

3. The temperature dropped 2 degrees from 7:00 P.M. to 8:00 P.M. The temperature was 52°F at 8:00 P.M. What was the temperature at 7:00 P.M.? Write your answer in the diagram below.

4:00 P.M.	5:00 P.M.	6:00 P.M.	7:00 P.M.	8:00 P.M.
−4 →	−2 →	−2 →	−2 →	
				52°F
← +4	← +2	← +2	← +2	

Name ______________________________

Work Backward (continued)

4. Find the temperature at 6:00 P.M., then 5:00 P.M., then 4:00 P.M. Write each in the diagram on the previous page.

5. What was the temperature at 4:00 P.M.? ______

Answer 6 and 7 to **look back and check** your solution to the problem.

6. The temperature dropped 2 degrees from 7:00 P.M. to 8:00 P.M., which means you subtract 2. When working backward from 8:00 P.M. to 7:00 P.M., do you add or subtract 2? ______

7. If the temperature was the one you found at 4:00 P.M. and changed as described in the problem, would it be 52°F at 8:00 P.M.? ______

Solve each problem.

8. It takes Josh 10 minutes to get ready for soccer practice and 25 minutes to bike to the field. He needs to eat a snack before he gets ready and that takes 15 minutes. Soccer practice is at 4:30. What time does Josh need to start eating his snack to get to soccer practice on time? ______

9. Lola took 45 minutes to get ready for school. She walked to school in 20 minutes and then waited 5 minutes before the bell rang at 8:55 A.M. What time did she get out of bed that morning?

______

10. The trip from your home to the museum takes 45 minutes. You need 1 hour and 30 minutes to tour a special exhibit in the museum. You want to finish the tour before 3:00 P.M. What is the latest time you should leave home to go to the museum?

______

Name ______________________________

Make and Test Generalizations

How are the polygons alike?

Polygon 1

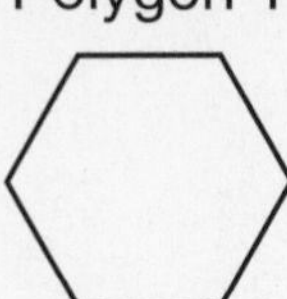

Polygon 2

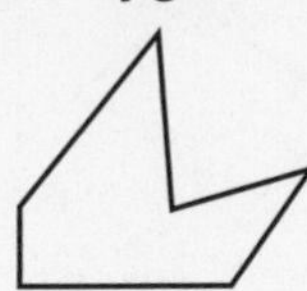

Polygon 3

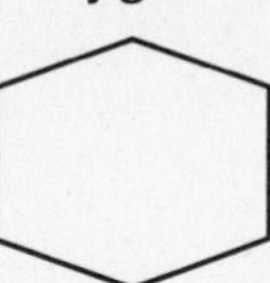

Solve by answering 1 to 5.

1. Complete the generalization about the polygons.

All the polygons have ______ sides.

2. Test the generalization.

Does Polygon 1 have 6 sides? ______ Polygon 2? ______

Polygon 3? ______

Since the generalization holds for all 3 polygons, it is true.

3. Test the following generalization: All the sides of each polygon are the same length.

Are all the sides of Polygon 1 the same length? ______

Are all the sides of Polygon 2 the same length? ______

Are all the sides of Polygon 3 the same length? ______

4. Is the conjecture true? ______

5. Reasoning Is the following generalization true? All the polygons have at least one obtuse angle. Explain.

Name ___________________________________

Make and Test Generalizations (continued)

Make a generalization about each set of figures. Test your generalization. If the generalization is not true, make another generalization until you find one that is true.

6. 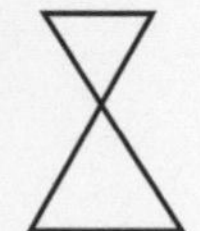  

7. N F A Z Y

8. 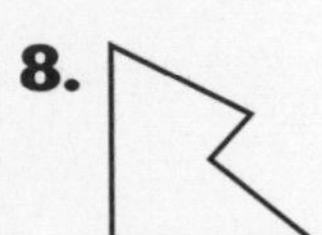 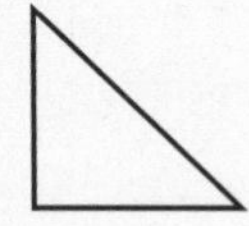 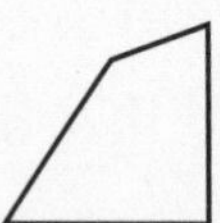

9. 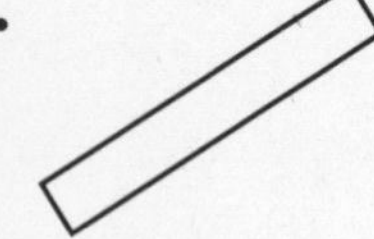  

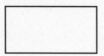

10. 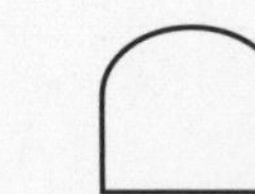 

Name ______________________________

Reasonableness

A container when empty weighs 150 pounds. If the container is filled with 312 pounds, what is the total weight of the container and its contents?

Solve by answering 1 to 7.

Answer 1 and 2 to **understand** the problem.

1. What do you know from reading the problem?

The empty container weighs ______ pounds.

The contents of the container weighs ______ pounds.

2. What do you need to find?

Answer 3 and 4 to **plan and solve** the problem.

3. How can you solve the problem? ____________________

4. What is the total weight of the container and its contents? ______ pounds

Answer 5 to 7 to **check** that your answer is reasonable.

5. Estimate 150 + 312 by rounding to the nearest hundred.

150 + 312 is about ______

6. Is your answer to the problem close to the estimate? ______

Since the answer of 462 is close to the estimate of 500, the answer 462 pounds is **reasonable**.

7. Did you answer the right question? ______

Name ____________________________

Reasonableness (continued)

Solve each problem. Then explain why your answer is reasonable.

8. Karen had some stickers. She gave 34 butterfly stickers and 27 flag stickers to Bill. How many stickers did Karen give to Bill?

9. Harold collects stamps. He has 32 stamps from the United States and 18 stamps from other countries. How many more United States stamps does Harold have than international stamps?

10. Some students took a survey about cats and dogs. They found that 87 students like dogs and 56 students like cats. How many students voted for cats or dogs?

11. On Friday, 214 people came to the concert. On Saturday, 298 people came. How many people came on both nights combined?

12. At TV City, a new television costs $629. At Discount Place, the same TV costs $498. How much more does the TV cost at TV City than at Discount Place?

Name ____________________

Write to Explain

Mr. Kerr wants to buy circus tickets for his family. Tickets cost $7 each. How much will it cost to buy 6 tickets?

Solve by answering 1 to 5.

Answer 1 and 2 to **understand** the problem.

1. What do you know from reading the problem?

Circus tickets cost ______ each.

2. What do you need to find?

Answer 3 and 4 to **plan and solve** the problem.

You can solve the problem by making a table.

3. Complete the table.

Number of tickets	1	2	3	4	5	6
Cost	$7	$14				

4. How much does it cost to buy 6 circus tickets? ______

Answer 5 to **look back** at the solution to the problem.

5. Fill in the blanks to complete the explanation of how to solve the problem.

One ticket cost $7, so two tickets cost $7 more. $7 + ______ = ______

Three ticket cost $7 more than 2 tickets. $14 + ______ = ______

Keep adding ______ to complete the table.

Six tickets cost ______.

Name ______________________________

Write to Explain (continued)

6. Fill in the blanks to complete the explanation of how to solve the problem.

Mollie is taller than Kristin and shorter than Mike. Ted is shorter than Mollie but taller than Kristin. Who is the tallest?

Mollie is taller than __________

and shorter than __________.

Draw a picture to show this information.

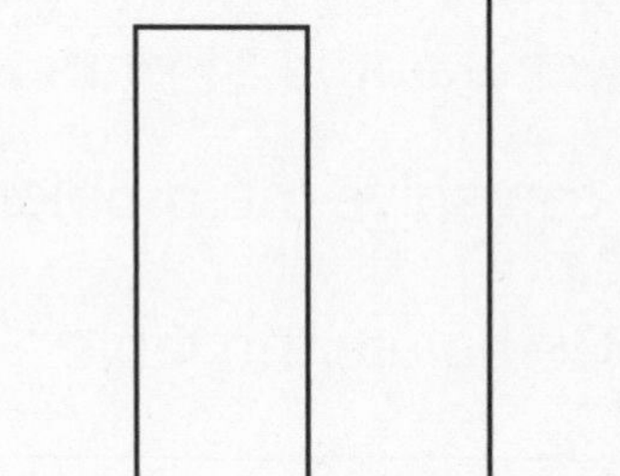

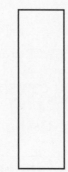

Ted is shorter than __________

but taller than __________.

Show this information in the picture.

The picture shows that the tallest is

__________.

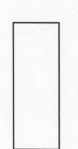

Write to explain.

7. Explain how the number of eggs changes as the number of dozens changes.

Dozens	1	2	3	4	5
Eggs	12	24	36	48	60

8. Four people can sit at each square table. Three tables are pushed together to form a long rectangular table. How many people can sit at this long table?